MW00604192

Your Daily TALK with God

Expressing gratitude to God is an important part of prayer. What things are you THANKFUL for today?

This is the place to note your worries, doubts, and things you can't control. LET God handle them today.

My TALK with God today	Day	Date

☐ Morning Prayer	☐ Evening Prayer	Choose one or more

Three Things I am THANKFUL for Today:

1.

2.

3.

LET go and let God handle it

I set these intentions for the day:

Don't let the day just happen to you - set intentions for the things you will do and be today!

_____
_____
_____
_____
_____
_____

ASK

What do I need forgiveness for?

Ask God to help with this challenge today.

We are commanded to ASK with sincerity of heart. Blessings will come when we ask in faith (James 1:5). Before your prayer look inward and answer these 3 topics.

People to keep in my prayers today.

KEEP communicating with God today

A kind deed done today.

Blessings I received today

Do not withhold good from those to whom it is due, when it is in your power to act. Proverbs 3:27

Now that you have finished your prayer, KEEP communicating with God today. Look for blessings, big and small - plus opportunities to help others.

My TALK with God today	Day	Date

☐ Morning Prayer	☐ Evening Prayer	Choose one or more	**ASK**

Three Things I am **THANKFUL** for Today:

1.

2.

3.

LET go and let God handle it

What do I need forgiveness for?

Ask God to help with this challenge today.

I set these intentions for the day:

_____

_____

_____

_____

_____

_____

People to keep in my prayers today.

KEEP communicating with God today

A kind deed done today.

_____

_____

_____

_____

_____

Blessings I received today

_____

_____

_____

_____

_____

Do not withhold good from those to whom it is due, when it is in your power to act. Proverbs 3:27

Faith 365 Bucket Journal
Your Daily TALK with God

©2021 by My Bucket Journals
Designed and printed in the USA. All rights reserved.

ISBN: 978-1-63933-043-0
Publisher: My Bucket Journals. LLC
PO Box 310, Hutto, Texas 78634

This publication may not be reproduced stored or transmitted in whole or in part, in any form or by any means, electronic, mechanical or otherwise, without prior written consent from the publisher and author.

Brief quotations may be included in a review. If in PDF form, it may be stored on your computer and you may keep one online digital copy. This publication may be printed for personal use only.

Disclaimer
The information in this book is based on the author's opinion, knowledge and experience. The publisher and the author will not be held liable for the use or misuse of the information contained herein.

Disclosure
This book may contain affiliate links. If you click through an affiliate link to a third-party website and make a purchase, the author may receive a small commission.

Cover photo ©DepositPhotos

The Faith 365 Bucket Journal gives you a place to have a daily TALK with God through prayer and record your impressions before and after. TALK stands for thankfulness, ask, let go, and keeping God in your day.

How to Use Your Faith 365 Bucket Journal

The daily pages are not dated so that you can start your Faith 365 Bucket Journal at any time

- Identify three things you are **Thankful** for each day. Expressing gratitude to God is an integral part of prayer. Mention these blessings in your prayer as you speak with God.
- We are commanded to **Ask** with sincerity of heart; blessings will come to us when we ask in faith (James 1:5)
  - We may need to ask for forgiveness for ourselves and also ask for our daily needs.
  - We may need to ask God to help with a specific challenge today.
  - There are people we want to remember in our prayers.
- Use this space to note your worries and things that may be bothering you; that you can't control. When you **Let** go and let God handle it, you can find peace.
- After your prayers, **Keep** God top of mind throughout the day and keep communicating with God throughout the day. You can do this by looking for blessings, big and small, and recognizing opportunities to help others.
- We've provided 365 daily scripture references to inspire your faith, encourage your service, and give you comfort in trials.

Do you find that you can go for days or weeks, letting life happen to you? What you intend to attract often shows up in the most unexpected ways. Setting **daily intentions** helps you be more in tune with your world and God's plan for you.

Not only will this bucket journal be a record of one year of hopes, dreams, struggles, and blessings, but it will also give you insight into how God works in your life through prayer.

My TALK with God today	Day	Date

☐ Morning Prayer	☐ Evening Prayer	Choose one or more	**ASK**

Three Things I am **THANKFUL** for Today:

1.

2.

3.

What do I need forgiveness for?

LET go and let God handle it

Ask God to help with this challenge today.

I set these intentions for the day:

_____

_____

_____

_____

_____

_____

People to keep in my prayers today.

KEEP communicating with God today

A kind deed done today.   Blessings I received today

_____ _____

_____ _____

_____ _____

_____ _____

_____ _____

Rejoice always, pray continually, give thanks in all circumstances; for this is God's will for you in Christ Jesus.
1 Thessalonians 5:16-18

My TALK with God today   **Day**   **Date**

☐ Morning Prayer	☐ Evening Prayer	Choose one or more

ASK

Three Things I am **THANKFUL** for Today:

1.

2.

3.

What do I need forgiveness for?

LET go and let God handle it

Ask God to help with this challenge today.

I set these intentions for the day:

_____

_____

_____

_____

_____

People to keep in my prayers today.

KEEP communicating with God today

A kind deed done today.

_____

_____

_____

_____

Blessings I received today

_____

_____

_____

_____

Then you will call on me and come and pray to me, and I will listen to you.
Jeremiah 29:12

My TALK with God today → **Day** **Date**

☐ Morning Prayer	☐ Evening Prayer	Choose one or more	**ASK**

Three Things I am **THANKFUL** for Today:

1.

2.

3.

LET go and let God handle it

I set these intentions for the day:

_____

_____

_____

_____

_____

_____

KEEP communicating with God today

A kind deed done today.   Blessings I received today

_____   _____

_____   _____

_____   _____

_____   _____

_____   _____

Be joyful in hope, patient in affliction, faithful in prayer. Romans 12:12

My TALK with God today

Day _____   **Date** _____

☐ Morning Prayer	☐ Evening Prayer	Choose one or more

Three Things I am **THANKFUL** for Today:

1.

2.

3.

LET go and let God handle it

I set these intentions for the day:

_____

_____

_____

_____

_____

_____

ASK

What do I need forgiveness for?

Ask God to help with this challenge today.

People to keep in my prayers today.

KEEP communicating with God today

A kind deed done today.

_____

_____

_____

_____

_____

Blessings I received today

_____

_____

_____

_____

_____

Let us then approach God's throne of grace with confidence, so that we may receive mercy and find grace to help us in our time of need.
Hebrews 4:16

My TALK with God today

	Day		Date

☐ Morning Prayer	☐ Evening Prayer	Choose one or more

ASK

Three Things I am **THANKFUL** for Today:

1.

2.

3.

What do I need forgiveness for?

LET go and let God handle it

Ask God to help with this challenge today.

I set these intentions for the day:

_____

_____

_____

_____

_____

_____

People to keep in my prayers today.

KEEP communicating with God today

A kind deed done today.

_____

_____

_____

_____

_____

Blessings I received today

_____

_____

_____

_____

_____

Whatever you ask in prayer, believe that you have received it, and it will be yours.
Mark 11:24

My TALK with God today → **Day** **Date**

☐ Morning Prayer	☐ Evening Prayer	Choose one or more

Three Things I am **THANKFUL** for Today:

1.

2.

3.

What do I need forgiveness for?

LET go and let God handle it

Ask God to help with this challenge today.

I set these intentions for the day:

_____

_____

_____

_____

_____

_____

People to keep in my prayers today.

KEEP communicating with God today

A kind deed done today.

_____

_____

_____

_____

_____

Blessings I received today

_____

_____

_____

_____

_____

Even though I walk through the valley of the shadow of death, I will fear no evil, for you are with me; your rod and your staff, they comfort me. Psalms 23:4

My TALK with God today

Day

Date

☐ **Morning Prayer**   ☐ **Evening Prayer**   Choose one or more

What do I need forgiveness for?

Three Things I am **THANKFUL** for Today:

1.

2.

3.

LET go and let God handle it

Ask God to help with this challenge today.

I set these intentions for the day:

_____

_____

_____

_____

_____

_____

People to keep in my prayers today.

KEEP communicating with God today

A kind deed done today.

_____

_____

_____

_____

_____

Blessings I received today

_____

_____

_____

_____

_____

Blessed are those who mourn, for they will be comforted.
Matthew 5:4

My TALK with God today

Day   **Date**

☐ Morning Prayer	☐ Evening Prayer	Choose one or more

ASK

Three Things I am **THANKFUL** for Today:

1.

2.

3.

What do I need forgiveness for?

LET go and let God handle it

Ask God to help with this challenge today.

I set these intentions for the day:

_____

_____

_____

_____

_____

_____

People to keep in my prayers today.

KEEP communicating with God today

A kind deed done today.

_____

_____

_____

_____

_____

Blessings I received today

_____

_____

_____

_____

_____

Therefore encourage one another and build each other up, just as in fact you are doing. 1 Thessalonians 5:11

My TALK with God today → **Day** **Date**

☐ Morning Prayer	☐ Evening Prayer	Choose one or more

ASK

Three Things I am **THANKFUL** for Today:
1.
2.
3.

What do I need forgiveness for?

LET go and let God handle it

Ask God to help with this challenge today.

I set these intentions for the day:

_____

_____

_____

_____

_____

_____

People to keep in my prayers today.

KEEP communicating with God today

A kind deed done today.	**Blessings I received today**
_____	_____
_____	_____
_____	_____
_____	_____
_____	_____

The world and its desires pass away, but whoever does the will of God lives forever.
1 John 2:17

My TALK with God today | **Day** | **Date**

☐ Morning Prayer	☐ Evening Prayer	Choose one or more

ASK

Three Things I am **THANKFUL** for Today:

1.

2.

3.

What do I need forgiveness for?

LET go and let God handle it

Ask God to help with this challenge today.

I set these intentions for the day:

_____

_____

_____

_____

_____

_____

People to keep in my prayers today.

KEEP communicating with God today

A kind deed done today.

_____

_____

_____

_____

Blessings I received today

_____

_____

_____

_____

When anxiety was great within me, your consolation brought me joy.
Psalms 94:19

My TALK with God today

Day   **Date**

☐ Morning Prayer	☐ Evening Prayer	Choose one or more

ASK

Three Things I am **THANKFUL** for Today:

1.

2.

3.

What do I need forgiveness for?

LET go and let God handle it

Ask God to help with this challenge today.

I set these intentions for the day:
_____
_____
_____
_____
_____
_____

People to keep in my prayers today.

KEEP communicating with God today

A kind deed done today.
_____
_____
_____
_____
_____

Blessings I received today
_____
_____
_____
_____
_____

They who wait for the Lord shall renew their strength; they shall mount up with wings like eagles; they shall run and not be.
Isaiah 40:31

My TALK with God today

Day _____   **Date** _____

☐ Morning Prayer	☐ Evening Prayer	Choose one or more

ASK

Three Things I am THANKFUL for Today:

1.

2.

3.

What do I need forgiveness for?

LET go and let God handle it

Ask God to help with this challenge today.

I set these intentions for the day:

_____

_____

_____

_____

_____

_____

People to keep in my prayers today.

KEEP communicating with God today

A kind deed done today.

_____

_____

_____

_____

_____

Blessings I received today

_____

_____

_____

_____

_____

The steadfast love of the Lord never ceases; his mercies never come to an end; they are new every morning; great is your faithfulness.
Lamentations 3:22-23

My TALK with God today ➜ **Day**   **Date**

☐ Morning Prayer	☐ Evening Prayer	Choose one or more

ASK

Three Things I am **THANKFUL** for Today:

1.

2.

3.

What do I need forgiveness for?

LET go and let God handle it

Ask God to help with this challenge today.

I set these intentions for the day:

_____
_____
_____
_____
_____
_____

People to keep in my prayers today.

KEEP communicating with God today

A kind deed done today.   Blessings I received today

_____   _____
_____   _____
_____   _____
_____   _____
_____   _____

Give thanks to the Lord, for he is good; his love endures forever.
1 Chronicles 16:34

My TALK with God today   **Day**   **Date**

☐ Morning Prayer	☐ Evening Prayer	Choose one or more

ASK

Three Things I am **THANKFUL** for Today:

1.

2.

3.

LET go and let God handle it

What do I need forgiveness for?

Ask God to help with this challenge today.

I set these intentions for the day:

_____

_____

_____

_____

_____

_____

People to keep in my prayers today.

KEEP communicating with God today

A kind deed done today.

_____

_____

_____

_____

Blessings I received today

_____

_____

_____

_____

May the Lord direct your hearts into God's love and Christ's perseverance.
2 Thessalonians 3:5

My TALK with God today

Day _____   **Date** _____

☐ Morning Prayer	☐ Evening Prayer	Choose one or more

ASK

What do I need forgiveness for?

Three Things I am **THANKFUL** for Today:
1.
2.
3.

LET go and let God handle it

Ask God to help with this challenge today.

I set these intentions for the day:

_____

_____

_____

_____

_____

_____

People to keep in my prayers today.

KEEP communicating with God today

A kind deed done today.

_____

_____

_____

_____

_____

Blessings I received today

_____

_____

_____

_____

_____

Whoever is patient has great understanding, but one who is quick-tempered displays folly.
Proverbs 14:29

My TALK with God today

Day

Date

- ☐ **Morning Prayer**
- ☐ **Evening Prayer**

Choose one or more

ASK

Three Things I am **THANKFUL** for Today:

1.

2.

3.

What do I need forgiveness for?

LET go and let God handle it

Ask God to help with this challenge today.

I set these intentions for the day:

_____

_____

_____

_____

_____

_____

People to keep in my prayers today.

KEEP communicating with God today

A kind deed done today.

_____

_____

_____

_____

_____

Blessings I received today

_____

_____

_____

_____

That according to the riches of his glory he may grant you to be strengthened with power through his Spirit in your inner being, so that Christ may dwell in your hearts through faith—that you, being rooted and grounded in love.
Ephesians 3:16-17

My TALK with God today | **Day** | **Date**

☐ Morning Prayer	☐ Evening Prayer	Choose one or more

ASK

Three Things I am **THANKFUL** for Today:

1.

2.

3.

What do I need forgiveness for?

LET go and let God handle it

Ask God to help with this challenge today.

I set these intentions for the day:

_____

_____

_____

_____

_____

_____

People to keep in my prayers today.

KEEP communicating with God today

A kind deed done today. | **Blessings I received today**

_____ _____

_____ _____

_____ _____

_____ _____

_____ _____

May the favor of the Lord our God rest on us; establish the work of our hands for us! Psalms 90:17

My TALK with God today | **Day** | **Date**

☐	Morning Prayer	☐	Evening Prayer	Choose one or more

ASK

Three Things I am **THANKFUL** for Today:

1.

2.

3.

What do I need forgiveness for?

LET go and let God handle it

Ask God to help with this challenge today.

I set these intentions for the day:

_____

_____

_____

_____

_____

_____

People to keep in my prayers today.

KEEP communicating with God today

A kind deed done today.

Blessings I received today

_____ _____

_____ _____

_____ _____

_____ _____

_____ _____

I will ask the Father, and he will give you another advocate to help you and be with you forever.
John 14:16

My TALK with God today ➤ **Day** | **Date**

☐ Morning Prayer	☐ Evening Prayer	Choose one or more

ASK

Three Things I am **THANKFUL** for Today:
1.
2.
3.

What do I need forgiveness for?

LET go and let God handle it

Ask God to help with this challenge today.

I set these intentions for the day:

_____

_____

_____

_____

_____

People to keep in my prayers today.

KEEP communicating with God today

A kind deed done today.   **Blessings I received today**

_____   _____

_____   _____

_____   _____

_____   _____

_____   _____

For we live by faith, not by sight.
2 Corinthians 5:7

My TALK with God today	Day	Date

☐ Morning Prayer	☐ Evening Prayer	Choose one or more	ASK

Three Things I am **THANKFUL** for Today:

1.

2.

3.

What do I need forgiveness for?

LET go and let God handle it

Ask God to help with this challenge today.

I set these intentions for the day:

_____

_____

_____

_____

_____

People to keep in my prayers today.

KEEP communicating with God today

A kind deed done today.

_____

_____

_____

_____

_____

Blessings I received today

_____

_____

_____

_____

_____

It is the Lord who goes before you. He will be with you; he will not leave you or forsake you. Do not fear or be dismayed.
Deuteronomy 5:33

My TALK with God today → **Day**   **Date**

☐ Morning Prayer	☐ Evening Prayer	Choose one or more

ASK

Three Things I am **THANKFUL** for Today:
1.
2.
3.

What do I need forgiveness for?

LET go and let God handle it

Ask God to help with this challenge today.

I set these intentions for the day:
_____
_____
_____
_____
_____
_____

People to keep in my prayers today.

KEEP communicating with God today

A kind deed done today.
_____
_____
_____
_____
_____

Blessings I received today
_____
_____
_____
_____
_____

For no word from God will ever fail.
Luke 1:37

My TALK with God today ➡️ **Day**   **Date**

☐ Morning Prayer	☐ Evening Prayer	Choose one or more

ASK

Three Things I am **THANKFUL** for Today:
1.
2.
3.

What do I need forgiveness for?

LET go and let God handle it

Ask God to help with this challenge today.

I set these intentions for the day:

_____
_____
_____
_____
_____
_____

People to keep in my prayers today.

KEEP communicating with God today

A kind deed done today.   **Blessings I received today**

_____   _____
_____   _____
_____   _____
_____   _____
_____   _____

Since we live by the Spirit, let us keep in step with the Spirit.
Galatians 5:25

My TALK with God today　　　Day　　　　　　　Date

☐ Morning Prayer	☐ Evening Prayer	Choose one or more

ASK

Three Things I am **THANKFUL** for Today:
1.
2.
3.

What do I need forgiveness for?

LET go and let God handle it

Ask God to help with this challenge today.

I set these intentions for the day:

_____

_____

_____

_____

_____

_____

People to keep in my prayers today.

KEEP communicating with God today

A kind deed done today.

_____

_____

_____

_____

_____

Blessings I received today

_____

_____

_____

_____

_____

In the same way, faith by itself, if it is not accompanied by action, is dead.
James 2:17

My TALK with God today	Day		Date

☐ Morning Prayer	☐ Evening Prayer	Choose one or more	**ASK**

Three Things I am **THANKFUL** for Today:

1.

2.

3.

What do I need forgiveness for?

LET go and let God handle it

Ask God to help with this challenge today.

I set these intentions for the day:

_____

_____

_____

_____

_____

_____

People to keep in my prayers today.

KEEP communicating with God today

A kind deed done today.

_____

_____

_____

_____

_____

Blessings I received today

_____

_____

_____

_____

_____

Whoever wants to become great among you must be your servant, and whoever wants to be first must be your slave.
Matthew 20:26 - 27

My TALK with God today

Day	Date

☐ Morning Prayer	☐ Evening Prayer	Choose one or more

ASK

Three Things I am **THANKFUL** for Today:

1.

2.

3.

What do I need forgiveness for?

LET go and let God handle it

Ask God to help with this challenge today.

I set these intentions for the day:

_____

_____

_____

_____

_____

_____

People to keep in my prayers today.

KEEP communicating with God today

A kind deed done today.	Blessings I received today
_____	_____
_____	_____
_____	_____
_____	_____
_____	_____

The Lord will rescue his servants; no one who takes refuge in him will be condemned.
Psalms 34:22

My TALK with God today   **Day**   **Date**

☐ Morning Prayer	☐ Evening Prayer	Choose one or more

ASK

Three Things I am **THANKFUL** for Today:

1.

2.

3.

What do I need forgiveness for?

LET go and let God handle it

Ask God to help with this challenge today.

I set these intentions for the day:

_____

_____

_____

_____

_____

_____

People to keep in my prayers today.

KEEP communicating with God today

A kind deed done today.

_____

_____

_____

_____

_____

Blessings I received today

_____

_____

_____

_____

_____

Do not merely listen to the word, and so deceive yourselves. Do what it says.
James 1:22

My TALK with God today	Day		Date

☐ Morning Prayer	☐ Evening Prayer	Choose one or more	ASK

Three Things I am **THANKFUL** for Today:

1.

2.

3.

What do I need forgiveness for?

LET go and let God handle it

Ask God to help with this challenge today.

I set these intentions for the day:

_____

_____

_____

_____

_____

_____

People to keep in my prayers today.

KEEP communicating with God today

A kind deed done today.   **Blessings I received today**

_____   _____

_____   _____

_____   _____

_____   _____

_____   _____

Stand firm, let nothing move you. Always give yourselves fully to the work of the Lord, because you know that your labor in the Lord is not in vain.
1 Corinthians 15:58

My TALK with God today | **Day** | **Date**

☐	Morning Prayer	☐	Evening Prayer	Choose one or more

ASK

Three Things I am **THANKFUL** for Today:

1.

2.

3.

What do I need forgiveness for?

LET go and let God handle it

Ask God to help with this challenge today.

I set these intentions for the day:

_____

_____

_____

_____

_____

_____

People to keep in my prayers today.

KEEP communicating with God today

A kind deed done today.   **Blessings I received today**

_____   _____

_____   _____

_____   _____

_____   _____

_____

Do not conform to the pattern of this world, but be transformed by the renewing of your mind. Then you will be able to test and approve what God's will is—his good, pleasing and perfect will. Romans 12:2

My TALK with God today | Day | Date

☐ Morning Prayer	☐ Evening Prayer	Choose one or more

ASK

Three Things I am **THANKFUL** for Today:

1.

2.

3.

What do I need forgiveness for?

LET go and let God handle it

Ask God to help with this challenge today.

I set these intentions for the day:

_____
_____
_____
_____
_____

People to keep in my prayers today.

KEEP communicating with God today

A kind deed done today.

Blessings I received today

_____   _____
_____   _____
_____   _____
_____   _____
_____   _____

Submit yourselves, then, to God. Resist the devil, and he will flee from you.
James 4:7

My TALK with God today | **Day** | **Date**

☐ Morning Prayer	☐ Evening Prayer	Choose one or more

ASK

Three Things I am **THANKFUL** for Today:
1.
2.
3.

What do I need forgiveness for?

LET go and let God handle it

Ask God to help with this challenge today.

I set these intentions for the day:

_____
_____
_____
_____
_____
_____

People to keep in my prayers today.

KEEP communicating with God today

A kind deed done today.	Blessings I received today
_____	_____
_____	_____
_____	_____
_____	_____
_____	_____

Blessed is everyone who fears the Lord, who walks in his ways!
Psalms 128:1

My TALK with God today → **Day**   **Date**

☐ Morning Prayer	☐ Evening Prayer	Choose one or more

Three Things I am **THANKFUL** for Today:
1.
2.
3.

What do I need forgiveness for?

LET go and let God handle it

Ask God to help with this challenge today.

I set these intentions for the day:
_____
_____
_____
_____
_____
_____

People to keep in my prayers today.

KEEP communicating with God today

A kind deed done today.   Blessings I received today
_____   _____
_____   _____
_____   _____
_____   _____
_____   _____

Whoever believes in the Son has eternal life, but whoever rejects the Son will not see life, for God's wrath remains on them.
John 3:36

My TALK with God today →   **Day**   **Date**

☐ Morning Prayer	☐ Evening Prayer	Choose one or more

ASK

Three Things I am **THANKFUL** for Today:

1.

2.

3.

What do I need forgiveness for?

LET go and let God handle it

Ask God to help with this challenge today.

I set these intentions for the day:

_____

_____

_____

_____

_____

_____

People to keep in my prayers today.

KEEP communicating with God today

A kind deed done today.

_____

_____

_____

_____

_____

Blessings I received today

_____

_____

_____

_____

_____

Guarding the paths of justice and watching over the way of his saints.
Proverbs 2:8

My TALK with God today | **Day** | **Date**

☐ Morning Prayer	☐ Evening Prayer	Choose one or more

ASK

Three Things I am **THANKFUL** for Today:

1.

2.

3.

What do I need forgiveness for?

LET go and let God handle it

Ask God to help with this challenge today.

I set these intentions for the day:

_____

_____

_____

_____

_____

_____

People to keep in my prayers today.

KEEP communicating with God today

A kind deed done today.

_____

_____

_____

_____

_____

Blessings I received today

_____

_____

_____

_____

_____

God settles the solitary in a home; he leads out the prisoners to prosperity, but the rebellious dwell in a parched land.
Psalms 68:6

My TALK with God today

Day

Date

☐ Morning Prayer

☐ Evening Prayer

Choose one or more

ASK

What do I need forgiveness for?

Three Things I am **THANKFUL** for Today:

1.

2.

3.

Ask God to help with this challenge today.

LET go and let God handle it

I set these intentions for the day:

_____

_____

_____

_____

_____

_____

People to keep in my prayers today.

KEEP communicating with God today

A kind deed done today.

_____

_____

_____

_____

_____

Blessings I received today

_____

_____

_____

_____

_____

If you believe, you will receive whatever you ask for in prayer. Matthew 21:22

My TALK with God today → **Day**   **Date**

☐ Morning Prayer	☐ Evening Prayer	Choose one or more

ASK

Three Things I am **THANKFUL** for Today:

1.

2.

3.

What do I need forgiveness for?

LET go and let God handle it

Ask God to help with this challenge today.

I set these intentions for the day:

_____

_____

_____

_____

_____

_____

People to keep in my prayers today.

KEEP communicating with God today

A kind deed done today.

_____

_____

_____

_____

_____

Blessings I received today

_____

_____

_____

_____

_____

You did not choose me, but I chose you and appointed you so that you might go and bear fruit—fruit that will last—and so that whatever you ask in my name the Father will give you
John 15:16

My TALK with God today	Day		Date

☐ Morning Prayer	☐ Evening Prayer	Choose one or more	ASK

Three Things I am **THANKFUL** for Today:

1.

2.

3.

LET go and let God handle it

ASK

What do I need forgiveness for?

Ask God to help with this challenge today.

I set these intentions for the day:

_____

_____

_____

_____

_____

_____

People to keep in my prayers today.

KEEP communicating with God today

A kind deed done today.

_____

_____

_____

_____

_____

Blessings I received today

_____

_____

_____

_____

_____

Give to everyone who asks you, and if anyone takes what belongs to you, do not demand it back
Luke 6:30

My TALK with God today   **Day**   **Date**

☐ Morning Prayer	☐ Evening Prayer	Choose one or more

ASK

Three Things I am **THANKFUL** for Today:
1.
2.
3.

What do I need forgiveness for?

LET go and let God handle it

Ask God to help with this challenge today.

I set these intentions for the day:
_____
_____
_____
_____
_____
_____

People to keep in my prayers today.

KEEP communicating with God today

A kind deed done today.   Blessings I received today
_____   _____
_____   _____
_____   _____
_____   _____
_____   _____

For those who are led by the Spirit of God are the children of God.
Romans 8:14

My TALK with God today **Day** **Date**

☐	Morning Prayer	☐	Evening Prayer	Choose one or more

ASK

Three Things I am **THANKFUL** for Today:

1.

2.

3.

What do I need forgiveness for?

LET go and let God handle it

Ask God to help with this challenge today.

I set these intentions for the day:

_____

_____

_____

_____

_____

People to keep in my prayers today.

KEEP communicating with God today

A kind deed done today.

_____

_____

_____

_____

Blessings I received today

_____

_____

_____

_____

He sent out his word and healed them; he rescued them from the grave.
Psalms 107:20

My TALK with God today ➤ **Day** | **Date**

☐ Morning Prayer	☐ Evening Prayer	Choose one or more	**ASK**

Three Things I am **THANKFUL** for Today:

1.

2.

3.

What do I need forgiveness for?

LET go and let God handle it

Ask God to help with this challenge today.

I set these intentions for the day:

_____

_____

_____

_____

_____

People to keep in my prayers today.

KEEP communicating with God today

A kind deed done today.   Blessings I received today

_____   _____

_____   _____

_____   _____

_____   _____

_____   _____

My prayer is not that you take them out of the world but that you protect them from the evil one.
John 17:15

My TALK with God today → **Day**

Date

☐ Morning Prayer	☐ Evening Prayer	Choose one or more

ASK

Three Things I am **THANKFUL** for Today:

1.

2.

3.

What do I need forgiveness for?

LET go and let God handle it

Ask God to help with this challenge today.

I set these intentions for the day:

_____

_____

_____

_____

_____

_____

People to keep in my prayers today.

KEEP communicating with God today

A kind deed done today.	Blessings I received today
_____	_____
_____	_____
_____	_____
_____	_____
_____	_____

To do what is right and just is more acceptable to the Lord than sacrifice.
Proverbs 21:3

My TALK with God today → **Day**   **Date**

☐ Morning Prayer	☐ Evening Prayer	Choose one or more

ASK

Three Things I am **THANKFUL** for Today:

1.

2.

3.

What do I need forgiveness for?

LET go and let God handle it

Ask God to help with this challenge today.

I set these intentions for the day:

_____

_____

_____

_____

_____

_____

People to keep in my prayers today.

KEEP communicating with God today

A kind deed done today.

_____

_____

_____

_____

_____

Blessings I received today

_____

_____

_____

_____

_____

Do not be deceived: God cannot be mocked. A man reaps what he sows.
Galatians 6:7

My TALK with God today → **Day** **Date**

☐ Morning Prayer	☐ Evening Prayer	Choose one or more

ASK

Three Things I am **THANKFUL** for Today:

1.

2.

3.

What do I need forgiveness for?

LET go and let God handle it

Ask God to help with this challenge today.

I set these intentions for the day:

_____

_____

_____

_____

_____

_____

People to keep in my prayers today.

KEEP communicating with God today

A kind deed done today.

_____

_____

_____

_____

_____

Blessings I received today

_____

_____

_____

_____

_____

Whoever eats my flesh and drinks my blood remains in me, and I in them.
John 6:56

My TALK with God today

Day

Date

☐ Morning Prayer
☐ Evening Prayer
Choose one or more

ASK

Three Things I am **THANKFUL** for Today:

1.

2.

3.

What do I need forgiveness for?

LET go and let God handle it

Ask God to help with this challenge today.

I set these intentions for the day:

_____

_____

_____

_____

_____

_____

People to keep in my prayers today.

KEEP communicating with God today

A kind deed done today.

_____

_____

_____

_____

_____

Blessings I received today

_____

_____

_____

_____

_____

Ask and it will be given to you; seek and you will find; knock and the door will be opened to you. Matthew 7:7

My TALK with God today

Day

Date

☐ Morning Prayer	☐ Evening Prayer	Choose one or more

ASK

Three Things I am **THANKFUL** for Today:

1.

2.

3.

LET go and let God handle it

What do I need forgiveness for?

Ask God to help with this challenge today.

I set these intentions for the day:

_____

_____

_____

_____

_____

_____

People to keep in my prayers today.

KEEP communicating with God today

A kind deed done today.

_____

_____

_____

_____

_____

Blessings I received today

_____

_____

_____

_____

_____

You shall not misuse the name of the Lord your God, for the Lord will not hold anyone guiltless who misuses his name.
Deuteronomy 5:11

My TALK with God today	Day	Date

☐ Morning Prayer	☐ Evening Prayer	Choose one or more

ASK

Three Things I am **THANKFUL** for Today:

What do I need forgiveness for?

1.

2.

3.

LET go and let God handle it

Ask God to help with this challenge today.

I set these intentions for the day:

_____

_____

_____

_____

_____

_____

People to keep in my prayers today.

KEEP communicating with God today

A kind deed done today.

_____

_____

_____

_____

_____

Blessings I received today

_____

_____

_____

_____

_____

Trust in the Lord and do good; dwell in the land and enjoy safe pasture.
Psalms 37:3

My TALK with God today

Day

Date

☐ Morning Prayer	☐ Evening Prayer	Choose one or more

ASK

Three Things I am THANKFUL for Today:

1.

2.

3.

LET go and let God handle it

What do I need forgiveness for?

Ask God to help with this challenge today.

I set these intentions for the day:

_____

_____

_____

_____

_____

_____

People to keep in my prayers today.

KEEP communicating with God today

A kind deed done today.

Blessings I received today

_____ _____

_____ _____

_____ _____

_____ _____

The Lord your God is with you, the Mighty Warrior who saves. He will take great delight in you; in his love he will no longer rebuke you, but will rejoice over you with singing
Zephaniah 3:17

My TALK with God today | **Day** | **Date**

☐ Morning Prayer	☐ Evening Prayer	Choose one or more

ASK

What do I need forgiveness for?

Three Things I am **THANKFUL** for Today:

1.

2.

3.

LET go and let God handle it

Ask God to help with this challenge today.

I set these intentions for the day:

_____

_____

_____

_____

_____

People to keep in my prayers today.

KEEP communicating with God today

A kind deed done today.

_____

_____

_____

_____

_____

Blessings I received today

_____

_____

_____

_____

_____

Do not let your hearts be troubled. You believe in God; believe also in me. John 14:1

My TALK with God today → **Day**   **Date**

☐ Morning Prayer	☐ Evening Prayer	Choose one or more

ASK

Three Things I am **THANKFUL** for Today:
1.
2.
3.

What do I need forgiveness for?

LET go and let God handle it

Ask God to help with this challenge today.

I set these intentions for the day:

_____

_____

_____

_____

_____

_____

People to keep in my prayers today.

KEEP communicating with God today

A kind deed done today.

_____

_____

_____

_____

_____

Blessings I received today

_____

_____

_____

_____

_____

For we believe that Jesus died and rose again, and so we believe that God will bring with Jesus those who have fallen asleep in him
1 Thessalonians 4:14

My TALK with God today

Day   **Date**

☐ Morning Prayer	☐ Evening Prayer	Choose one or more

Three Things I am **THANKFUL** for Today:

1.

2.

3.

LET go and let God handle it

ASK

What do I need forgiveness for?

Ask God to help with this challenge today.

People to keep in my prayers today.

I set these intentions for the day:

_____

_____

_____

_____

_____

_____

KEEP communicating with God today

A kind deed done today.

_____

_____

_____

_____

_____

Blessings I received today

_____

_____

_____

_____

_____

Trust in the Lord with all your heart and lean not on your own understanding; in all your ways submit to him, and he will make your paths straight.
Proverbs 37:5 - 6

My TALK with God today

Day   **Date**

☐ Morning Prayer	☐ Evening Prayer	Choose one or more

ASK

Three Things I am **THANKFUL** for Today:

1.

2.

3.

What do I need forgiveness for?

LET go and let God handle it

Ask God to help with this challenge today.

I set these intentions for the day:

_____

_____

_____

_____

_____

_____

People to keep in my prayers today.

KEEP communicating with God today

A kind deed done today.   **Blessings I received today**

_____   _____

_____   _____

_____   _____

_____   _____

_____   _____

For it is with your heart that you believe and are justified, and it is with your mouth that you profess your faith and are saved.
Romans 10:10

My TALK with God today

Day _____ **Date** _____

☐ Morning Prayer	☐ Evening Prayer	Choose one or more

ASK

What do I need forgiveness for?

Three Things I am **THANKFUL** for Today:
1.
2.
3.

LET go and let God handle it

Ask God to help with this challenge today.

I set these intentions for the day:

_____
_____
_____
_____
_____
_____

People to keep in my prayers today.

KEEP communicating with God today

A kind deed done today.

_____
_____
_____
_____
_____

Blessings I received today

_____
_____
_____
_____
_____

Though you have not seen him, you love him; and even though you do not see him now, you believe in him and are filled with an inexpressible and glorious joy, for you are receiving the end result of your faith, the salvation of your souls.
1 Peter 1:8-9

My TALK with God today

Day

Date

☐	Morning Prayer	☐	Evening Prayer	Choose one or more

ASK

What do I need forgiveness for?

Three Things I am **THANKFUL** for Today:

1.

2.

3.

LET go and let God handle it

Ask God to help with this challenge today.

I set these intentions for the day:

_____

_____

_____

_____

_____

People to keep in my prayers today.

KEEP communicating with God today

A kind deed done today.

_____

_____

_____

_____

_____

Blessings I received today

_____

_____

_____

_____

_____

I remain confident of this: I will see the goodness of the Lord in the land of the living.
Psalms 27:13

My TALK with God today

Day

Date

☐ Morning Prayer	☐ Evening Prayer	Choose one or more

ASK

Three Things I am **THANKFUL** for Today:

1.

2.

3.

What do I need forgiveness for?

LET go and let God handle it

Ask God to help with this challenge today.

I set these intentions for the day:

_____
_____
_____
_____
_____
_____

People to keep in my prayers today.

KEEP communicating with God today

A kind deed done today.

_____
_____
_____
_____
_____

Blessings I received today

_____
_____
_____
_____
_____

Give, and it will be given to you. A good measure, pressed down, shaken together and running over, will be poured into your lap. For with the measure you use, it will be measured to you.
Luke 6:38

My TALK with God today ➤ **Day** | **Date**

☐	Morning Prayer	☐	Evening Prayer	Choose one or more

ASK

Three Things I am **THANKFUL** for Today:

1.

2.

3.

LET go and let God handle it

What do I need forgiveness for?

Ask God to help with this challenge today.

I set these intentions for the day:

_____

_____

_____

_____

_____

_____

People to keep in my prayers today.

KEEP communicating with God today

A kind deed done today.

_____

_____

_____

_____

Blessings I received today

_____

_____

_____

_____

Praise be to the God and Father of our Lord Jesus Christ, the Father of compassion and the God of all comfort, who comforts us in all our troubles, so that we can comfort those in any trouble with the comfort we ourselves receive from God. 2 Corinthians 1:3-4

My TALK with God today ➤ **Day** | **Date**

☐ Morning Prayer	☐ Evening Prayer	Choose one or more

ASK

Three Things I am **THANKFUL** for Today:
1.
2.
3.

What do I need forgiveness for?

LET go and let God handle it

Ask God to help with this challenge today.

I set these intentions for the day:

_____

_____

_____

_____

_____

People to keep in my prayers today.

KEEP communicating with God today

A kind deed done today.	Blessings I received today
_____	_____
_____	_____
_____	_____
_____	_____
_____	_____

A gentle answer turns away wrath, but a harsh word stirs up anger.
Proverbs 15:1

My TALK with God today	Day	Date

☐ Morning Prayer	☐ Evening Prayer	Choose one or more	**ASK**

Three Things I am **THANKFUL** for Today:

1.

2.

3.

What do I need forgiveness for?

LET go and let God handle it

Ask God to help with this challenge today.

I set these intentions for the day:

_____

_____

_____

_____

_____

People to keep in my prayers today.

KEEP communicating with God today

A kind deed done today.

_____

_____

_____

_____

_____

Blessings I received today

_____

_____

_____

_____

_____

It is better to take refuge in the Lord than to trust in humans.
Psalms 118:8

My TALK with God today

Day _____

Date _____

☐ Morning Prayer	☐ Evening Prayer	Choose one or more

ASK

Three Things I am **THANKFUL** for Today:
1.
2.
3.

What do I need forgiveness for?

LET go and let God handle it

Ask God to help with this challenge today.

I set these intentions for the day:

_____

_____

_____

_____

_____

_____

People to keep in my prayers today.

KEEP communicating with God today

A kind deed done today.	Blessings I received today
_____	_____
_____	_____
_____	_____
_____	_____
_____	_____

The Lord is good, a refuge in times of trouble. He cares for those who trust in him.
Nahum 1:7

My TALK with God today **Day** **Date**

☐ Morning Prayer	☐ Evening Prayer	Choose one or more

ASK

Three Things I am **THANKFUL** for Today:

1.

2.

3.

What do I need forgiveness for?

LET go and let God handle it

Ask God to help with this challenge today.

I set these intentions for the day:

_____

_____

_____

_____

_____

_____

People to keep in my prayers today.

KEEP communicating with God today

A kind deed done today.

_____

_____

_____

_____

_____

Blessings I received today

_____

_____

_____

_____

_____

Keep me safe, my God, for in you I take refuge.
Psalms 16:1

My TALK with God today → **Day** **Date**

☐ Morning Prayer	☐ Evening Prayer	Choose one or more

ASK

Three Things I am THANKFUL for Today:

1.

2.

3.

What do I need forgiveness for?

LET go and let God handle it

Ask God to help with this challenge today.

I set these intentions for the day:

_____

_____

_____

_____

_____

_____

People to keep in my prayers today.

KEEP communicating with God today

A kind deed done today.

_____

_____

_____

_____

_____

Blessings I received today

_____

_____

_____

_____

_____

The Lord will keep you from all harm— he will watch over your life; the Lord will watch over your coming and going both now and forevermore.
Psalms 121:7-8

My TALK with God today	Day	Date

☐ Morning Prayer	☐ Evening Prayer	Choose one or more

ASK

Three Things I am **THANKFUL** for Today:
1.
2.
3.

What do I need forgiveness for?

LET go and let God handle it

Ask God to help with this challenge today.

I set these intentions for the day:

_____

_____

_____

_____

_____

_____

People to keep in my prayers today.

KEEP communicating with God today

A kind deed done today.

_____

_____

_____

_____

_____

Blessings I received today

_____

_____

_____

_____

_____

Now faith is confidence in what we hope for and assurance about what we do not see.
Hebrews 11:1

My TALK with God today

Day **Date**

☐ Morning Prayer	☐ Evening Prayer	Choose one or more

ASK

Three Things I am **THANKFUL** for Today:

1.

2.

3.

What do I need forgiveness for?

LET go and let God handle it

Ask God to help with this challenge today.

I set these intentions for the day:

_____

_____

_____

_____

_____

_____

People to keep in my prayers today.

KEEP communicating with God today

A kind deed done today.

_____

_____

_____

_____

_____

Blessings I received today

_____

_____

_____

_____

_____

Hope deferred makes the heart sick, but a longing fulfilled is a tree of life.
Proverbs 13:12

My TALK with God today

Day

Date

☐ Morning Prayer	☐ Evening Prayer	Choose one or more

ASK

Three Things I am **THANKFUL** for Today:

1.

2.

3.

What do I need forgiveness for?

LET go and let God handle it

Ask God to help with this challenge today.

I set these intentions for the day:

_____

_____

_____

_____

_____

_____

People to keep in my prayers today.

KEEP communicating with God today

A kind deed done today.

_____

_____

_____

_____

_____

Blessings I received today

_____

_____

_____

_____

_____

Guide me in your truth and teach me, for you are God my Savior, and my hope is in you all day long.
Psalms 25:5

My TALK with God today	Day	Date

☐ Morning Prayer	☐ Evening Prayer	Choose one or more

ASK

Three Things I am **THANKFUL** for Today:

1.

2.

3.

LET go and let God handle it

What do I need forgiveness for?

Ask God to help with this challenge today.

I set these intentions for the day:

_____

_____

_____

_____

_____

_____

People to keep in my prayers today.

KEEP communicating with God today

A kind deed done today.

Blessings I received today

_____ _____

_____ _____

_____ _____

_____ _____

_____ _____

Whoever conceals their sins does not prosper, but the one who confesses and renounces them finds mercy.
Proverbs 28:13

My TALK with God today

Day **Date**

☐ Morning Prayer	☐ Evening Prayer	Choose one or more

ASK

What do I need forgiveness for?

Three Things I am **THANKFUL** for Today:
1.
2.
3.

LET go and let God handle it

Ask God to help with this challenge today.

I set these intentions for the day:

_____

_____

_____

_____

_____

People to keep in my prayers today.

KEEP communicating with God today

A kind deed done today.	Blessings I received today
_____	_____
_____	_____
_____	_____
_____	_____
_____	_____

Let the wicked forsake their ways and the unrighteous their thoughts. Let them turn to the Lord, and he will have mercy on them, and to our God, for he will freely pardon.
Isaiah 55:7

My TALK with God today	Day	Date

☐ Morning Prayer	☐ Evening Prayer	Choose one or more

ASK

Three Things I am **THANKFUL** for Today:

1.

2.

3.

What do I need forgiveness for?

LET go and let God handle it

Ask God to help with this challenge today.

I set these intentions for the day:

_____

_____

_____

_____

_____

People to keep in my prayers today.

KEEP communicating with God today

A kind deed done today.

_____

_____

_____

_____

_____

Blessings I received today

_____

_____

_____

_____

_____

Give us today our daily bread. And forgive us our debts, as we also have forgiven our debtors. Matthew 6:11-12

My TALK with God today ➡️ Day   Date

| ☐ Morning Prayer | ☐ Evening Prayer | Choose one or more | **ASK** |

Three Things I am **THANKFUL** for Today:

1.

2.

3.

LET go and let God handle it

What do I need forgiveness for?

I set these intentions for the day:

_____
_____
_____
_____
_____
_____

Ask God to help with this challenge today.

People to keep in my prayers today.

KEEP communicating with God today

A kind deed done today.	Blessings I received today
_____	_____
_____	_____
_____	_____
_____	_____
_____	_____

Do not withhold your mercy from me, Lord; may your love and faithfulness always protect me.
Psalms 40:11

My TALK with God today → **Day** **Date**

☐ Morning Prayer	☐ Evening Prayer	Choose one or more

ASK

Three Things I am **THANKFUL** for Today:

1.

2.

3.

What do I need forgiveness for?

LET go and let God handle it

Ask God to help with this challenge today.

I set these intentions for the day:

_____

_____

_____

_____

_____

_____

People to keep in my prayers today.

KEEP communicating with God today

A kind deed done today.

_____

_____

_____

_____

_____

Blessings I received today

_____

_____

_____

_____

_____

Unless you believe that I am who I claim to be, you will die in your sins.
John 8:24

My TALK with God today

Day _____ **Date** _____

☐ Morning Prayer	☐ Evening Prayer	Choose one or more

Three Things I am **THANKFUL** for Today:

1.

2.

3.

LET go and let God handle it

I set these intentions for the day:

_____

_____

_____

_____

_____

_____

KEEP communicating with God today

A kind deed done today.

_____

_____

_____

_____

Blessings I received today

_____

_____

_____

_____

ASK

What do I need forgiveness for?

Ask God to help with this challenge today.

People to keep in my prayers today.

For by grace you have been saved through faith. And this is not your own doing; it is the gift of God, not a result of works, so that no one may boast.
Ephesians 2:8-9

My TALK with God today | **Day** | **Date**

☐ Morning Prayer	☐ Evening Prayer	Choose one or more

ASK

Three Things I am **THANKFUL** for Today:

1.

2.

3.

What do I need forgiveness for?

LET go and let God handle it

Ask God to help with this challenge today.

I set these intentions for the day:

_____

_____

_____

_____

_____

_____

People to keep in my prayers today.

KEEP communicating with God today

A kind deed done today.   Blessings I received today

_____   _____

_____   _____

_____   _____

_____   _____

_____   _____

The apostles said to the Lord,
"Increase our faith!"
Luke 17:5

My TALK with God today

Day

Date

☐ Morning Prayer	☐ Evening Prayer	Choose one or more

ASK

Three Things I am **THANKFUL** for Today:

1.

2.

3.

What do I need forgiveness for?

LET go and let God handle it

Ask God to help with this challenge today.

I set these intentions for the day:

_____
_____
_____
_____
_____
_____

People to keep in my prayers today.

KEEP communicating with God today

A kind deed done today.

Blessings I received today

_____ _____
_____ _____
_____ _____
_____ _____
_____ _____

Surely there is a future, and your hope will not be cut off.
Proverbs 23:18

My TALK with God today → Day   Date

☐ Morning Prayer	☐ Evening Prayer	Choose one or more	**ASK**

Three Things I am THANKFUL for Today:

1.

2.

3.

LET go and let God handle it

I set these intentions for the day:

_____

_____

_____

_____

_____

_____

KEEP communicating with God today

A kind deed done today.

_____

_____

_____

_____

_____

Blessings I received today

_____

_____

_____

_____

_____

ASK

What do I need forgiveness for?

Ask God to help with this challenge today.

People to keep in my prayers today.

Therefore do not be anxious about tomorrow, for tomorrow will be anxious for itself. Sufficient for the day is its own trouble.
Matthew 6:34

My TALK with God today

Day

Date

☐	Morning Prayer	☐	Evening Prayer	Choose one or more

ASK

Three Things I am **THANKFUL** for Today:

1.

2.

3.

What do I need forgiveness for?

LET go and let God handle it

Ask God to help with this challenge today.

I set these intentions for the day:

_____

_____

_____

_____

_____

_____

People to keep in my prayers today.

KEEP communicating with God today

A kind deed done today.

Blessings I received today

_____   _____

_____   _____

_____   _____

_____   _____

_____   _____

The Lord is a refuge for the oppressed, a stronghold in times of trouble.
Psalms 9:9-10

My TALK with God today

Day

Date

☐ Morning Prayer	☐ Evening Prayer	Choose one or more

ASK

Three Things I am **THANKFUL** for Today:

1.

2.

3.

LET go and let God handle it

What do I need forgiveness for?

Ask God to help with this challenge today.

I set these intentions for the day:

_____

_____

_____

_____

_____

_____

People to keep in my prayers today.

KEEP communicating with God today

A kind deed done today.

_____

_____

_____

_____

Blessings I received today

_____

_____

_____

_____

Seek the LORD and his strength; seek his presence continually!
1 Chronicles 16:11

My TALK with God today	Day		Date

ASK

☐ Morning Prayer	☐ Evening Prayer	Choose one or more

What do I need forgiveness for?

Three Things I am **THANKFUL** for Today:
1.
2.
3.

LET go and let God handle it

Ask God to help with this challenge today.

I set these intentions for the day:

_____

_____

_____

_____

_____

_____

People to keep in my prayers today.

KEEP communicating with God today

A kind deed done today.

_____

_____

_____

_____

_____

Blessings I received today

_____

_____

_____

_____

_____

For to set the mind on the flesh is death, but to set the mind on the Spirit is life and peace.
Romans 8:6

My TALK with God today → **Day**   **Date**

	ASK

☐ **Morning Prayer**   ☐ **Evening Prayer**   Choose one or more

What do I need forgiveness for?

Three Things I am **THANKFUL** for Today:
1.
2.
3.

LET go and let God handle it

Ask God to help with this challenge today.

I set these intentions for the day:

_____

_____

_____

People to keep in my prayers today.

_____

_____

_____

KEEP communicating with God today

A kind deed done today.   **Blessings I received today**

_____   _____

_____   _____

_____   _____

_____   _____

_____   _____

Devote yourselves to prayer, being watchful and thankful.
Colossians 4:2

My TALK with God today → Day   Date

☐ Morning Prayer	☐ Evening Prayer	Choose one or more

ASK

Three Things I am **THANKFUL** for Today:

1.

2.

3.

What do I need forgiveness for?

LET go and let God handle it

Ask God to help with this challenge today.

I set these intentions for the day:

_____

_____

_____

_____

_____

_____

People to keep in my prayers today.

KEEP communicating with God today

A kind deed done today.

_____

_____

_____

_____

_____

Blessings I received today

_____

_____

_____

_____

_____

The Lord is near to all who call on him, to all who call on him in truth.
Psalms 145:18

My TALK with God today → **Day** **Date**

☐ Morning Prayer	☐ Evening Prayer	Choose one or more

ASK

What do I need forgiveness for?

Three Things I am **THANKFUL** for Today:

1.

2.

3.

LET go and let God handle it

Ask God to help with this challenge today.

I set these intentions for the day:

_____

_____

_____

_____

_____

_____

People to keep in my prayers today.

KEEP communicating with God today

A kind deed done today.   **Blessings I received today**

_____   _____

_____   _____

_____   _____

_____   _____

_____   _____

For just as we share abundantly in the sufferings of Christ, so also our comfort abounds through Christ.
2 Corinthians 1:5

My TALK with God today

Day

Date

☐ Morning Prayer	☐ Evening Prayer	Choose one or more

ASK

Three Things I am **THANKFUL** for Today:

1.

2.

3.

What do I need forgiveness for?

LET go and let God handle it

Ask God to help with this challenge today.

I set these intentions for the day:

_____

_____

_____

_____

_____

_____

People to keep in my prayers today.

KEEP communicating with God today

A kind deed done today.

_____

_____

_____

_____

_____

Blessings I received today

_____

_____

_____

_____

_____

For where two or three gather in my name, there am I with them.
Matthew 18:20

My TALK with God today → **Day** | **Date**

☐ **Morning Prayer**	☐ **Evening Prayer**	Choose one or more

ASK

Three Things I am **THANKFUL** for Today:

1.

2.

3.

What do I need forgiveness for?

LET go and let God handle it

Ask God to help with this challenge today.

I set these intentions for the day:

_____

_____

_____

_____

_____

_____

People to keep in my prayers today.

KEEP communicating with God today

A kind deed done today.

_____

_____

_____

_____

_____

Blessings I received today

_____

_____

_____

_____

_____

Whoever believes in me, as Scripture has said, rivers of living water will flow from within them.
John 7:38

My TALK with God today | **Day** | **Date**

☐ Morning Prayer	☐ Evening Prayer	Choose one or more

ASK

Three Things I am **THANKFUL** for Today:
1.
2.
3.

What do I need forgiveness for?

LET go and let God handle it

Ask God to help with this challenge today.

I set these intentions for the day:

_____

_____

_____

_____

_____

_____

People to keep in my prayers today.

KEEP communicating with God today

A kind deed done today.	Blessings I received today
_____	_____
_____	_____
_____	_____
_____	_____
_____	_____

The end of all things is near. Therefore be alert and of sober mind so that you may pray.
1 Peter 4:7

My TALK with God today   **Day**   **Date**

☐ Morning Prayer	☐ Evening Prayer	Choose one or more

ASK

Three Things I am **THANKFUL** for Today:

1.

2.

3.

What do I need forgiveness for?

LET go and let God handle it

Ask God to help with this challenge today.

I set these intentions for the day:

_____

_____

_____

_____

_____

_____

People to keep in my prayers today.

KEEP communicating with God today

A kind deed done today.

_____

_____

_____

_____

_____

Blessings I received today

_____

_____

_____

_____

_____

Above all else, guard your heart, for everything you do flows from it.
Proverbs 4:23

My TALK with God today   **Day**   **Date**

☐ Morning Prayer	☐ Evening Prayer	Choose one or more

ASK

Three Things I am **THANKFUL** for Today:

1.

2.

3.

What do I need forgiveness for?

LET go and let God handle it

Ask God to help with this challenge today.

I set these intentions for the day:
_____
_____
_____
_____
_____
_____

People to keep in my prayers today.

KEEP communicating with God today

A kind deed done today.   **Blessings I received today**
_____   _____
_____   _____
_____   _____
_____   _____
_____   _____

Love your enemies and pray for those who persecute you.
Matthew 5:44

My TALK with God today ➤	Day	Date

❑ Morning Prayer	❑ Evening Prayer	Choose one or more

ASK

Three Things I am **THANKFUL** for Today:

1.

2.

3.

What do I need forgiveness for?

LET go and let God handle it

Ask God to help with this challenge today.

I set these intentions for the day:

_____

_____

_____

_____

_____

People to keep in my prayers today.

KEEP communicating with God today

A kind deed done today.

_____

_____

_____

_____

_____

Blessings I received today

_____

_____

_____

_____

_____

This poor man called, and the Lord heard him; he saved him out of all his troubles.
Psalms 34:6

My TALK with God today → **Day**   **Date**

❑ Morning Prayer	❑ Evening Prayer	Choose one or more

ASK

Three Things I am **THANKFUL** for Today:
1.
2.
3.

What do I need forgiveness for?

LET go and let God handle it

Ask God to help with this challenge today.

I set these intentions for the day:

_____

_____

_____

_____

_____

_____

People to keep in my prayers today.

KEEP communicating with God today

A kind deed done today.	Blessings I received today
_____	_____
_____	_____
_____	_____
_____	_____
_____	_____

Lead us not into temptation, but deliver us from the evil one.
Matthew 6:13

My TALK with God today → **Day** **Date**

☐ Morning Prayer	☐ Evening Prayer	Choose one or more

ASK

Three Things I am **THANKFUL** for Today:
1.
2.
3.

What do I need
forgiveness for?

LET go and let God handle it

Ask God to help with this
challenge today.

I set these intentions for the day:

_____

_____

_____

_____

_____

_____

People to keep in my
prayers today.

KEEP communicating with God today

A kind deed done today.   **Blessings I received today**

_____   _____

_____   _____

_____   _____

_____   _____

_____   _____

Everyone who calls on
the name of the Lord
will be saved.
Acts 2:21

My TALK with God today → **Day** **Date**

☐	Morning Prayer	☐	Evening Prayer	Choose one or more

ASK

Three Things I am **THANKFUL** for Today:

What do I need forgiveness for?

1.

2.

3.

LET go and let God handle it

Ask God to help with this challenge today.

I set these intentions for the day:

_____

_____

_____

_____

_____

_____

People to keep in my prayers today.

KEEP communicating with God today

A kind deed done today.   Blessings I received today

_____   _____

_____   _____

_____   _____

_____   _____

_____   _____

Good will come to those who are generous and lend freely, who conduct their affairs with justice.
Psalms 112:5

My TALK with God today	Day		Date

☐ Morning Prayer	☐ Evening Prayer	Choose one or more	ASK

Three Things I am **THANKFUL** for Today:

1.

2.

3.

What do I need forgiveness for?

LET go and let God handle it

Ask God to help with this challenge today.

I set these intentions for the day:
_____
_____
_____
_____
_____
_____

People to keep in my prayers today.

KEEP communicating with God today

A kind deed done today.
_____
_____
_____
_____
_____

Blessings I received today
_____
_____
_____
_____
_____

The Lord will fight for you; you need only to be still.
Exodus 14:14

My TALK with God today

Day	Date

☐ Morning Prayer	☐ Evening Prayer	Choose one or more

ASK

Three Things I am **THANKFUL** for Today:

1.

2.

3.

What do I need forgiveness for?

LET go and let God handle it

Ask God to help with this challenge today.

I set these intentions for the day:

_____

_____

_____

_____

_____

_____

People to keep in my prayers today.

KEEP communicating with God today

A kind deed done today.

_____

_____

_____

_____

_____

Blessings I received today

_____

_____

_____

_____

_____

Above all else, guard your heart, for everything you do flows from it. Proverbs 4:23

My TALK with God today

Day   **Date**

☐ Morning Prayer	☐ Evening Prayer	Choose one or more

ASK

Three Things I am **THANKFUL** for Today:

1.

2.

3.

What do I need forgiveness for?

LET go and let God handle it

Ask God to help with this challenge today.

I set these intentions for the day:

_____

_____

_____

_____

_____

_____

People to keep in my prayers today.

KEEP communicating with God today

A kind deed done today.   **Blessings I received today**

_____ _____

_____ _____

_____ _____

_____ _____

_____ _____

I will not leave you as orphans;
I will come to you.
John 14:18

My TALK with God today ➤ **Day** | **Date**

☐ Morning Prayer	☐ Evening Prayer	Choose one or more

ASK

Three Things I am **THANKFUL** for Today:

1.

2.

3.

What do I need forgiveness for?

LET go and let God handle it

Ask God to help with this challenge today.

I set these intentions for the day:

_____
_____
_____
_____
_____
_____

People to keep in my prayers today.

KEEP communicating with God today

A kind deed done today.

_____
_____
_____
_____
_____

Blessings I received today

_____
_____
_____
_____
_____

May the grace of the Lord Jesus Christ, and the love of God, and the fellowship of the Holy Spirit be with you all.
2 Corinthians 13:14

My TALK with God today | **Day** | **Date**

☐ Morning Prayer	☐ Evening Prayer	Choose one or more

ASK

Three Things I am **THANKFUL** for Today:
1.
2.
3.

What do I need forgiveness for?

LET go and let God handle it

Ask God to help with this challenge today.

I set these intentions for the day:

_____
_____
_____
_____
_____

People to keep in my prayers today.

KEEP communicating with God today

A kind deed done today.   **Blessings I received today**

_____   _____
_____   _____
_____   _____
_____   _____
_____   _____

The Lord is with you when you are with him. If you seek him, he will be found by you, but if you forsake him, he will forsake you.
2 Chronicles 15:2

My TALK with God today

Day

Date

☐ Morning Prayer	☐ Evening Prayer	Choose one or more

ASK

Three Things I am **THANKFUL** for Today:
1.
2.
3.

What do I need forgiveness for?

LET go and let God handle it

Ask God to help with this challenge today.

I set these intentions for the day:

_____

_____

_____

_____

_____

People to keep in my prayers today.

KEEP communicating with God today

A kind deed done today.	Blessings I received today
_____	_____
_____	_____
_____	_____
_____	_____
_____	_____

All your words are true; all your righteous laws are eternal.
Psalms 119:160

My TALK with God today — **Day** — **Date**

☐ Morning Prayer	☐ Evening Prayer	Choose one or more

ASK

Three Things I am **THANKFUL** for Today:

1.

2.

3.

What do I need forgiveness for?

LET go and let God handle it

Ask God to help with this challenge today.

I set these intentions for the day:

_____

_____

_____

_____

_____

_____

People to keep in my prayers today.

KEEP communicating with God today

A kind deed done today.   **Blessings I received today**

_____   _____

_____   _____

_____   _____

_____   _____

_____   _____

Peacemakers who sow in peace reap a harvest of righteousness. James 3:18

My TALK with God today **Day** **Date**

☐ Morning Prayer	☐ Evening Prayer	Choose one or more

ASK

Three Things I am **THANKFUL** for Today:

1.

2.

3.

What do I need forgiveness for?

LET go and let God handle it

Ask God to help with this challenge today.

I set these intentions for the day:
_____
_____
_____
_____
_____
_____

People to keep in my prayers today.

KEEP communicating with God today

A kind deed done today.
_____
_____
_____
_____
_____

Blessings I received today
_____
_____
_____
_____
_____

Blessed are those who hunger and thirst for righteousness, for they will be filled.
Matthew 5:6

My TALK with God today → **Day**   **Date**

☐ Morning Prayer	☐ Evening Prayer	Choose one or more

ASK

Three Things I am **THANKFUL** for Today:

1.

2.

3.

What do I need forgiveness for?

LET go and let God handle it

Ask God to help with this challenge today.

I set these intentions for the day:
_____
_____
_____
_____
_____
_____

People to keep in my prayers today.

KEEP communicating with God today

A kind deed done today.   Blessings I received today
_____   _____
_____   _____
_____   _____
_____   _____
_____   _____

Speak up and judge fairly; defend the rights of the poor and needy.
Proverbs 31:9

My TALK with God today | **Day** | **Date**

☐ Morning Prayer | ☐ Evening Prayer | Choose one or more

ASK

Three Things I am **THANKFUL** for Today:

1.

2.

3.

What do I need forgiveness for?

LET go and let God handle it

Ask God to help with this challenge today.

I set these intentions for the day:

_____

_____

_____

_____

_____

_____

People to keep in my prayers today.

KEEP communicating with God today

A kind deed done today.

_____

_____

_____

_____

_____

Blessings I received today

_____

_____

_____

_____

No discipline seems pleasant at the time, but painful. Later on, however, it produces a harvest of righteousness and peace for those who have been trained by it. Hebrews 12:11

My TALK with God today **Day** **Date**

☐ Morning Prayer	☐ Evening Prayer	Choose one or more

ASK

Three Things I am **THANKFUL** for Today:

1.

2.

3.

What do I need forgiveness for?

LET go and let God handle it

Ask God to help with this challenge today.

I set these intentions for the day:

_____
_____
_____
_____
_____
_____

People to keep in my prayers today.

KEEP communicating with God today

A kind deed done today.

_____
_____
_____
_____
_____

Blessings I received today

_____
_____
_____
_____
_____

The Lord is my shepherd, I lack nothing. He makes me lie down in green pastures, he leads me beside quiet waters.
Psalms 23:1-2

My TALK with God today

Day

Date

☐ Morning Prayer	☐ Evening Prayer	Choose one or more	**ASK**

Three Things I am **THANKFUL** for Today:

1.

2.

3.

What do I need forgiveness for?

LET go and let God handle it

Ask God to help with this challenge today.

I set these intentions for the day:

_____

_____

_____

_____

_____

_____

People to keep in my prayers today.

KEEP communicating with God today

A kind deed done today.

Blessings I received today

_____   _____

_____   _____

_____   _____

_____   _____

_____   _____

They gathered the church together and reported all that God had done through them and how he had opened a door of faith to the Gentiles.

My TALK with God today	Day		Date

☐ Morning Prayer	☐ Evening Prayer	Choose one or more	ASK

Three Things I am **THANKFUL** for Today:

1.

2.

3.

What do I need forgiveness for?

LET go and let God handle it

Ask God to help with this challenge today.

I set these intentions for the day:

_____

_____

_____

_____

_____

_____

People to keep in my prayers today.

KEEP communicating with God today

A kind deed done today.   **Blessings I received today**

_____   _____

_____   _____

_____   _____

_____   _____

_____   _____

You are the light of the world. A town built on a hill cannot be hidden.
Matthew 5:14

My TALK with God today | **Day** | **Date**

| ☐ | Morning Prayer | ☐ | Evening Prayer | Choose one or more | **ASK** |

What do I need
forgiveness for?

Three Things I am **THANKFUL** for Today:

1.

2.

3.

LET go and let God handle it

Ask God to help with this
challenge today.

I set these intentions for the day:

_____

_____

_____

_____

_____

_____

People to keep in my
prayers today.

KEEP communicating with God today

A kind deed done today.   Blessings I received today

_____ _____

_____ _____

_____ _____

_____ _____

_____ _____

The grass withers and
the flowers fall, but
the word of our God
endures forever.
Isaiah 40:8

My TALK with God today	Day	Date

☐ Morning Prayer	☐ Evening Prayer	Choose one or more

ASK

Three Things I am **THANKFUL** for Today:

1.

2.

3.

What do I need forgiveness for?

LET go and let God handle it

Ask God to help with this challenge today.

I set these intentions for the day:
_____
_____
_____
_____
_____
_____

People to keep in my prayers today.

KEEP communicating with God today

A kind deed done today.   Blessings I received today
_____   _____
_____   _____
_____   _____
_____   _____
_____   _____

The Lord is righteous in all his ways and faithful in all he does.
Psalms 145:17

My TALK with God today → **Day** **Date**

☐ Morning Prayer	☐ Evening Prayer	Choose one or more

ASK

Three Things I am **THANKFUL** for Today:

1.

2.

3.

What do I need forgiveness for?

LET go and let God handle it

Ask God to help with this challenge today.

I set these intentions for the day:

_____

_____

_____

_____

_____

_____

People to keep in my prayers today.

KEEP communicating with God today

A kind deed done today.

_____

_____

_____

_____

_____

Blessings I received today

_____

_____

_____

_____

_____

Everyone who sins breaks the law; in fact, sin is lawlessness.
1 John 3:4

My TALK with God today ➤ **Day**   **Date**

☐ Morning Prayer	☐ Evening Prayer	Choose one or more

ASK

Three Things I am **THANKFUL** for Today:

1.

2.

3.

What do I need forgiveness for?

LET go and let God handle it

Ask God to help with this challenge today.

I set these intentions for the day:

_____

_____

_____

_____

_____

_____

People to keep in my prayers today.

KEEP communicating with God today

A kind deed done today.

_____

_____

_____

_____

_____

Blessings I received today

_____

_____

_____

_____

_____

The prospect of the righteous is joy, but the hopes of the wicked come to nothing.
Proverbs 10:28

My TALK with God today

Day _____ **Date** _____

☐ Morning Prayer	☐ Evening Prayer	Choose one or more

ASK

Three Things I am **THANKFUL** for Today:

1.

2.

3.

What do I need forgiveness for?

LET go and let God handle it

Ask God to help with this challenge today.

I set these intentions for the day:

_____

_____

_____

_____

_____

_____

People to keep in my prayers today.

KEEP communicating with God today

A kind deed done today.

_____

_____

_____

_____

_____

Blessings I received today

_____

_____

_____

_____

_____

For we live by faith, not by sight.
2 Corinthians 5:7

My TALK with God today	Day		Date

☐ Morning Prayer	☐ Evening Prayer	Choose one or more	**ASK**

Three Things I am **THANKFUL** for Today:	**What do I need forgiveness for?**
1.	
2.	
3.	

LET go and let God handle it

Ask God to help with this challenge today.

I set these intentions for the day:

_____

_____

_____

_____ **People to keep in my prayers today.**

_____

_____

KEEP communicating with God today

A kind deed done today.	Blessings I received today
_____	_____
_____	_____
_____	_____
_____	_____
_____	_____

I am not saying this because I am in need, for I have learned to be content whatever the circumstances. Philippians 4:11

My TALK with God today ➤ **Day** _____ **Date** _____

☐ Morning Prayer	☐ Evening Prayer	Choose one or more

ASK

Three Things I am **THANKFUL** for Today:

1.

2.

3.

What do I need forgiveness for?

LET go and let God handle it

Ask God to help with this challenge today.

I set these intentions for the day:

_____

_____

_____

_____

_____

_____

People to keep in my prayers today.

KEEP communicating with God today

A kind deed done today.

_____

_____

_____

_____

_____

Blessings I received today

_____

_____

_____

_____

_____

The Lord makes firm the steps of the one who delights in him.
Psalms 37:23

My TALK with God today ➤ **Day** **Date**

☐ Morning Prayer	☐ Evening Prayer	Choose one or more	**ASK**

Three Things I am **THANKFUL** for Today:	What do I need forgiveness for?
1.	
2.	
3.	

LET go and let God handle it

Ask God to help with this challenge today.

I set these intentions for the day:

_____

_____

_____

People to keep in my prayers today.

_____

_____

_____

KEEP communicating with God today

A kind deed done today.	Blessings I received today
_____	_____
_____	_____
_____	_____
_____	_____
_____	_____

Look to the Lord and his strength; seek his face always.
1 Chronicles 16:11

My TALK with God today	Day		Date

☐ Morning Prayer	☐ Evening Prayer	Choose one or more	ASK

Three Things I am **THANKFUL** for Today:

1.

2.

3.

ASK

What do I need forgiveness for?

LET go and let God handle it

Ask God to help with this challenge today.

I set these intentions for the day:

_____

_____

_____

_____

_____

People to keep in my prayers today.

KEEP communicating with God today

A kind deed done today.

_____

_____

_____

_____

_____

Blessings I received today

_____

_____

_____

_____

_____

Wealth is worthless in the day of wrath, but righteousness delivers from death.
Proverbs 11:4

My TALK with God today

Day

Date

☐ Morning Prayer	☐ Evening Prayer	Choose one or more

ASK

Three Things I am **THANKFUL** for Today:

1.

2.

3.

What do I need forgiveness for?

LET go and let God handle it

Ask God to help with this challenge today.

I set these intentions for the day:

_____

_____

_____

_____

_____

_____

People to keep in my prayers today.

KEEP communicating with God today

A kind deed done today.

Blessings I received today

_____   _____

_____   _____

_____   _____

_____   _____

Love the Lord your God with all your heart ,and with all your soul, and with all your mind, and with all your strength.
Mark 12:30

My TALK with God today | **Day** | **Date**

☐	Morning Prayer	☐	Evening Prayer	Choose one or more

ASK

Three Things I am **THANKFUL** for Today:

1.

2.

3.

What do I need forgiveness for?

LET go and let God handle it

Ask God to help with this challenge today.

I set these intentions for the day:

_____

_____

_____

_____

_____

_____

People to keep in my prayers today.

KEEP communicating with God today

A kind deed done today.

_____

_____

_____

_____

_____

Blessings I received today

_____

_____

_____

_____

_____

The Lord gives strength to his people; the Lord blesses his people with peace.
Psalms 29:11

My TALK with God today **Day** **Date**

☐ Morning Prayer	☐ Evening Prayer	Choose one or more	**ASK**

Three Things I am **THANKFUL** for Today:

1.

2.

3.

LET go and let God handle it

What do I need forgiveness for?

Ask God to help with this challenge today.

I set these intentions for the day:

_____

_____

_____

_____

_____

_____

People to keep in my prayers today.

KEEP communicating with God today

A kind deed done today.   Blessings I received today

_____   _____

_____   _____

_____   _____

_____   _____

_____   _____

What is impossible with man is possible with God.
Luke 18:27

My TALK with God today → **Day** | **Date**

☐	Morning Prayer	☐	Evening Prayer	Choose one or more

ASK

Three Things I am **THANKFUL** for Today:
1.
2.
3.

What do I need forgiveness for?

LET go and let God handle it

Ask God to help with this challenge today.

I set these intentions for the day:

_____

_____

_____

_____

_____

_____

People to keep in my prayers today.

KEEP communicating with God today

A kind deed done today.	Blessings I received today
_____	_____
_____	_____
_____	_____
_____	_____
_____	_____

This is the confidence we have in approaching God: that if we ask anything according to his will, he hears us.
1 John 5:14

My TALK with God today ➤ **Day**   **Date**

☐ Morning Prayer	☐ Evening Prayer	Choose one or more

Three Things I am **THANKFUL** for Today:
1.
2.
3.

LET go and let God handle it

I set these intentions for the day:

_____
_____
_____
_____
_____
_____

ASK

What do I need forgiveness for?

Ask God to help with this challenge today.

People to keep in my prayers today.

KEEP communicating with God today

A kind deed done today.

_____
_____
_____
_____
_____

Blessings I received today

_____
_____
_____
_____
_____

Faith is confidence in what we hope for and assurance about what we do not see.
Hebrews 11:1

My TALK with God today

Day

Date

☐ Morning Prayer	☐ Evening Prayer	Choose one or more

ASK

Three Things I am **THANKFUL** for Today:

1.

2.

3.

What do I need forgiveness for?

LET go and let God handle it

Ask God to help with this challenge today.

I set these intentions for the day:

_____

_____

_____

_____

_____

_____

People to keep in my prayers today.

KEEP communicating with God today

A kind deed done today.

_____

_____

_____

_____

_____

Blessings I received today

_____

_____

_____

_____

_____

You are my hiding place; you will protect me from trouble and surround me with songs of deliverance. Psalms 32:7

My TALK with God today | **Day** | **Date**

☐ Morning Prayer	☐ Evening Prayer	Choose one or more

ASK

Three Things I am **THANKFUL** for Today:

1.

2.

3.

What do I need forgiveness for?

LET go and let God handle it

Ask God to help with this challenge today.

I set these intentions for the day:

_____

_____

_____

_____

_____

_____

People to keep in my prayers today.

KEEP communicating with God today

A kind deed done today.

Blessings I received today

_____ _____

_____ _____

_____ _____

_____ _____

_____ _____

Speak for those who cannot speak for themselves for the rights of all who are destitute. Speak up and judge fairly; defend the rights of the poor and needy. Proverbs 31:8 - 9

My TALK with God today →	**Day**	**Date**

☐ **Morning Prayer**	☐ **Evening Prayer**	Choose one or more	**ASK**

Three Things I am **THANKFUL** for Today:

1.

2.

3.

What do I need forgiveness for?

LET go and let God handle it

Ask God to help with this challenge today.

I set these intentions for the day:

_____

_____

_____

_____

_____

_____

People to keep in my prayers today.

KEEP communicating with God today

A kind deed done today.

_____

_____

_____

_____

_____

Blessings I received today

_____

_____

_____

_____

_____

Whoever welcomes one such child in my name welcomes me. Matthew 18:5

My TALK with God today	Day	Date

☐ Morning Prayer	☐ Evening Prayer	Choose one or more	**ASK**

Three Things I am **THANKFUL** for Today:
1.
2.
3.

What do I need forgiveness for?

LET go and let God handle it

Ask God to help with this challenge today.

I set these intentions for the day:
_____
_____
_____
_____
_____
_____

People to keep in my prayers today.

KEEP communicating with God today

A kind deed done today.

Blessings I received today
_____ _____
_____ _____
_____ _____
_____ _____
_____ _____

Though one may be overpowered, two can defend themselves. A cord of three strands is not quickly broken. Ecclesiastes 4:12

My TALK with God today

Day

Date

☐ Morning Prayer ☐ Evening Prayer | Choose one or more

ASK

Three Things I am **THANKFUL** for Today:

1.

2.

3.

What do I need forgiveness for?

LET go and let God handle it

Ask God to help with this challenge today.

I set these intentions for the day:

_____

_____

_____

_____

_____

_____

People to keep in my prayers today.

KEEP communicating with God today

A kind deed done today. | Blessings I received today

_____ _____

_____ _____

_____ _____

_____ _____

I will instruct you and teach you in the way you should go; I will counsel you with my loving eye on you.
Psalms 32:8

My TALK with God today | **Day** | **Date**

☐	Morning Prayer	☐	Evening Prayer	Choose one or more

Three Things I am **THANKFUL** for Today:

What do I need forgiveness for?

1.

2.

3.

LET go and let God handle it

Ask God to help with this challenge today.

I set these intentions for the day:

_____

_____

_____

_____

_____

_____

People to keep in my prayers today.

KEEP communicating with God today

A kind deed done today.

_____

_____

_____

_____

_____

Blessings I received today

_____

_____

_____

_____

_____

Wealth and honor come from you; you are the ruler of all things. In your hands are strength and power to exalt and give strength to all.
1 Chronicles 29:12

My TALK with God today | **Day** | **Date**

☐ Morning Prayer	☐ Evening Prayer	Choose one or more

ASK

Three Things I am **THANKFUL** for Today:
1.
2.
3.

What do I need forgiveness for?

LET go and let God handle it

Ask God to help with this challenge today.

I set these intentions for the day:

_____

_____

_____

_____

_____

_____

People to keep in my prayers today.

KEEP communicating with God today

A kind deed done today.

_____

_____

_____

_____

_____

Blessings I received today

_____

_____

_____

_____

_____

You then, my son, be strong in the grace that is in Christ Jesus. 2 Timothy 2:1

My TALK with God today → **Day**   **Date**

☐ Morning Prayer	☐ Evening Prayer	Choose one or more

Three Things I am **THANKFUL** for Today:

1.

2.

3.

LET go and let God handle it

I set these intentions for the day:
_____
_____
_____
_____
_____
_____

KEEP communicating with God today

A kind deed done today.
_____
_____
_____
_____
_____

Blessings I received today
_____
_____
_____
_____
_____

ASK

What do I need forgiveness for?

Ask God to help with this challenge today.

People to keep in my prayers today.

The Almighty is beyond our reach and exalted in power; in his justice and great righteousness, he does not oppress.
Job 37:23

My TALK with God today

Day

Date

☐	Morning Prayer	☐	Evening Prayer	Choose one or more

ASK

Three Things I am **THANKFUL** for Today:

1.

2.

3.

What do I need forgiveness for?

LET go and let God handle it

Ask God to help with this challenge today.

I set these intentions for the day:

_____

_____

_____

_____

_____

_____

People to keep in my prayers today.

KEEP communicating with God today

A kind deed done today.

Blessings I received today

_____   _____

_____   _____

_____   _____

_____   _____

Commit to the Lord whatever you do, and he will establish your plans.
Proverbs 16:3

My TALK with God today

Day

Date

☐ Morning Prayer	☐ Evening Prayer	Choose one or more

ASK

Three Things I am **THANKFUL** for Today:

1.

2.

3.

What do I need forgiveness for?

LET go and let God handle it

Ask God to help with this challenge today.

I set these intentions for the day:
_____
_____
_____
_____
_____
_____

People to keep in my prayers today.

KEEP communicating with God today

A kind deed done today.   Blessings I received today
_____   _____
_____   _____
_____   _____
_____   _____
_____   _____

Your word is a lamp
for my feet,
a light on my path.
Psalms 119:105

My TALK with God today

Day

Date

☐ Morning Prayer ☐ Evening Prayer Choose one or more

ASK

Three Things I am **THANKFUL** for Today:

1.

2.

3.

What do I need forgiveness for?

LET go and let God handle it

Ask God to help with this challenge today.

I set these intentions for the day:

_____

_____

_____

_____

_____

_____

People to keep in my prayers today.

KEEP communicating with God today

A kind deed done today.
_____
_____
_____
_____
_____

Blessings I received today
_____
_____
_____
_____
_____

The unfolding of your words gives light; it gives understanding to the simple.
Psalms 119:130

My TALK with God today

Day

Date

☐ Morning Prayer ☐ Evening Prayer Choose one or more

ASK

Three Things I am **THANKFUL** for Today:

1.

2.

3.

What do I need forgiveness for?

LET go and let God handle it

Ask God to help with this challenge today.

I set these intentions for the day:

_____

_____

_____

_____

_____

_____

People to keep in my prayers today.

KEEP communicating with God today

A kind deed done today.

_____

_____

_____

_____

_____

Blessings I received today

_____

_____

_____

_____

_____

You are already clean because of the word I have spoken to you.
John 15:3

My TALK with God today | **Day** | **Date**

☐ Morning Prayer	☐ Evening Prayer	Choose one or more

ASK

Three Things I am **THANKFUL** for Today:

1.

2.

3.

What do I need forgiveness for?

LET go and let God handle it

Ask God to help with this challenge today.

I set these intentions for the day:

_____

_____

_____

_____

_____

_____

People to keep in my prayers today.

KEEP communicating with God today

A kind deed done today.

_____

_____

_____

_____

_____

Blessings I received today

_____

_____

_____

_____

_____

Be kind and compassionate to one another, forgiving each other, just as in Christ God forgave you.
Ephesians 4:32

My TALK with God today

Day

Date

- [ ] Morning Prayer
- [ ] Evening Prayer

Choose one or more

ASK

What do I need forgiveness for?

Three Things I am **THANKFUL** for Today:

1.

2.

3.

LET go and let God handle it

Ask God to help with this challenge today.

I set these intentions for the day:

_____

_____

_____

_____

_____

People to keep in my prayers today.

KEEP communicating with God today

A kind deed done today.

Blessings I received today

_____   _____

_____   _____

_____   _____

_____   _____

_____   _____

Repent, then, and turn to God, so that your sins may be wiped out, that times of refreshing may come from the Lord. Acts 3:19

My TALK with God today	Day	Date

☐ Morning Prayer	☐ Evening Prayer	Choose one or more

ASK

Three Things I am **THANKFUL** for Today:

1.

2.

3.

What do I need forgiveness for?

LET go and let God handle it

Ask God to help with this challenge today.

I set these intentions for the day:

_____

_____

_____

_____

_____

People to keep in my prayers today.

KEEP communicating with God today

A kind deed done today.

_____

_____

_____

_____

_____

Blessings I received today

_____

_____

_____

_____

_____

Blessed is the one whose transgressions are forgiven, whose sins are covered. Psalms 32:1

My TALK with God today ➤ **Day**   **Date**

☐ Morning Prayer	☐ Evening Prayer	Choose one or more

ASK

Three Things I am **THANKFUL** for Today:

1.

2.

3.

What do I need forgiveness for?

LET go and let God handle it

Ask God to help with this challenge today.

I set these intentions for the day:

_____

_____

_____

_____

_____

_____

People to keep in my prayers today.

KEEP communicating with God today

A kind deed done today.

_____

_____

_____

_____

_____

Blessings I received today

_____

_____

_____

_____

_____

if you do not forgive others their sins, your Father will not forgive your sins.
Matthew 6:15

My TALK with God today → **Day** | | **Date**

☐ Morning Prayer	☐ Evening Prayer	Choose one or more

ASK

Three Things I am **THANKFUL** for Today:
1.
2.
3.

What do I need forgiveness for?

LET go and let God handle it

Ask God to help with this challenge today.

I set these intentions for the day:
_____
_____
_____
_____
_____
_____

People to keep in my prayers today.

KEEP communicating with God today

A kind deed done today.   **Blessings I received today**
_____   _____
_____   _____
_____   _____
_____   _____

What a person desires
is unfailing love;
better to be poor than
a liar.
Proverbs 19:22

My TALK with God today → **Day** _____ **Date** _____

☐ Morning Prayer	☐ Evening Prayer	Choose one or more

ASK

Three Things I am **THANKFUL** for Today:

1.

2.

3.

What do I need forgiveness for?

LET go and let God handle it

Ask God to help with this challenge today.

I set these intentions for the day:

_____

_____

_____

_____

_____

_____

People to keep in my prayers today.

KEEP communicating with God today

A kind deed done today.

_____

_____

_____

_____

_____

Blessings I received today

_____

_____

_____

_____

_____

Cast your cares on the Lord and he will sustain you; he will never let the righteous be shaken.
Psalms 55:22

My TALK with God today

Day

Date

☐ Morning Prayer	☐ Evening Prayer	Choose one or more

ASK

Three Things I am **THANKFUL** for Today:

1.

2.

3.

What do I need forgiveness for?

LET go and let God handle it

Ask God to help with this challenge today.

I set these intentions for the day:

_____

_____

_____

_____

_____

_____

People to keep in my prayers today.

KEEP communicating with God today

A kind deed done today.

_____

_____

_____

_____

_____

Blessings I received today

_____

_____

_____

_____

_____

The Lord himself goes before you and will be with you; he will never leave you nor forsake you. Do not be afraid; do not be discouraged. Deuteronomy 31:8

My TALK with God today

Day	Date

☐ Morning Prayer	☐ Evening Prayer	Choose one or more	ASK

Three Things I am **THANKFUL** for Today:

1.

2.

3.

LET go and let God handle it

I set these intentions for the day:

_____

_____

_____

_____

_____

_____

KEEP communicating with God today

A kind deed done today.	Blessings I received today
_____	_____
_____	_____
_____	_____
_____	_____
_____	_____

What do I need forgiveness for?

Ask God to help with this challenge today.

People to keep in my prayers today.

The integrity of the upright guides them, but the unfaithful are destroyed by their duplicity.
Proverbs 11:3

My TALK with God today

Day

Date

☐ Morning Prayer	☐ Evening Prayer	Choose one or more

ASK

Three Things I am **THANKFUL** for Today:

1.

2.

3.

What do I need forgiveness for?

LET go and let God handle it

Ask God to help with this challenge today.

I set these intentions for the day:

_____

_____

_____

_____

_____

_____

People to keep in my prayers today.

KEEP communicating with God today

A kind deed done today.

_____

_____

_____

_____

_____

Blessings I received today

_____

_____

_____

_____

_____

For those who are led by the Spirit of God are the children of God.
Romans 8:14

My TALK with God today	**Day**		**Date**

☐ Morning Prayer	☐ Evening Prayer	Choose one or more	**ASK**

Three Things I am **THANKFUL** for Today:
1.
2.
3.

What do I need forgiveness for?

LET go and let God handle it

Ask God to help with this challenge today.

I set these intentions for the day:

_____

_____

_____

_____

_____

People to keep in my prayers today.

KEEP communicating with God today

A kind deed done today.   **Blessings I received today**

_____   _____

_____   _____

_____   _____

_____   _____

_____   _____

A gossip betrays a confidence, but a trustworthy person keeps a secret.
Proverbs 11:13

My TALK with God today

Day

Date

☐ Morning Prayer	☐ Evening Prayer	Choose one or more

ASK

Three Things I am **THANKFUL** for Today:

1.

2.

3.

What do I need forgiveness for?

LET go and let God handle it

Ask God to help with this challenge today.

I set these intentions for the day:

_____

_____

_____

_____

_____

_____

People to keep in my prayers today.

KEEP communicating with God today

A kind deed done today.

Blessings I received today

_____ _____

_____ _____

_____ _____

_____ _____

_____ _____

For he satisfies the thirsty and fills the hungry with good things.
Psalms 107:9

My TALK with God today	Day	Date

☐ Morning Prayer	☐ Evening Prayer	Choose one or more	**ASK**

Three Things I am **THANKFUL** for Today:

1.

2.

3.

LET go and let God handle it

ASK

What do I need forgiveness for?

Ask God to help with this challenge today.

I set these intentions for the day:

_____

_____

_____

_____

_____

People to keep in my prayers today.

KEEP communicating with God today

A kind deed done today.   **Blessings I received today**

_____   _____

_____   _____

_____   _____

_____   _____

_____   _____

May the Lord our God be with us as he was with our ancestors; may he never leave us nor forsake us.
1 Kings 8:57

My TALK with God today

Day _____   **Date** _____

☐ Morning Prayer	☐ Evening Prayer	Choose one or more

Three Things I am **THANKFUL** for Today:

1.

2.

3.

LET go and let God handle it

I set these intentions for the day:

_____

_____

_____

_____

_____

_____

KEEP communicating with God today

A kind deed done today.

_____

_____

_____

_____

Blessings I received today

_____

_____

_____

_____

ASK

What do I need forgiveness for?

Ask God to help with this challenge today.

People to keep in my prayers today.

God is our refuge and strength, an ever-present help in trouble.
Psalms 46:1

My TALK with God today → **Day** **Date**

☐ Morning Prayer	☐ Evening Prayer	Choose one or more

ASK

Three Things I am **THANKFUL** for Today:

1.

2.

3.

What do I need forgiveness for?

LET go and let God handle it

Ask God to help with this challenge today.

I set these intentions for the day:

_____

_____

_____

_____

_____

_____

People to keep in my prayers today.

KEEP communicating with God today

A kind deed done today.

_____

_____

_____

_____

_____

Blessings I received today

_____

_____

_____

_____

_____

Gracious words are a honeycomb, sweet to the soul and healing to the bones.
Proverbs 16:24

My TALK with God today →	Day	Date

☐ Morning Prayer	☐ Evening Prayer	Choose one or more

ASK

Three Things I am **THANKFUL** for Today:

What do I need forgiveness for?

1.

2.

3.

LET go and let God handle it

Ask God to help with this challenge today.

I set these intentions for the day:

_____

_____

_____

_____

_____

_____

People to keep in my prayers today.

KEEP communicating with God today

A kind deed done today.

Blessings I received today

_____ _____

_____ _____

_____ _____

_____ _____

_____ _____

You will be enriched in every way so that you can be generous on every occasion, and through us your generosity will result in thanksgiving to God.
2 Corinthians 9:11

My TALK with God today

Day   **Date**

☐ Morning Prayer	☐ Evening Prayer	Choose one or more

ASK

What do I need forgiveness for?

Three Things I am THANKFUL for Today:

1.

2.

3.

LET go and let God handle it

Ask God to help with this challenge today.

I set these intentions for the day:

_____

_____

_____

_____

_____

_____

People to keep in my prayers today.

KEEP communicating with God today

A kind deed done today.

_____

_____

_____

_____

_____

Blessings I received today

_____

_____

_____

_____

_____

Let those who love the Lord hate evil, for he guards the lives of his faithful ones and delivers them from the hand of the wicked.
Psalms 97:10

My TALK with God today

Day

Date

☐ Morning Prayer

☐ Evening Prayer

Choose one or more

Three Things I am **THANKFUL** for Today:

1.

2.

3.

LET go and let God handle it

What do I need forgiveness for?

Ask God to help with this challenge today.

I set these intentions for the day:

_____

_____

_____

_____

_____

_____

People to keep in my prayers today.

KEEP communicating with God today

A kind deed done today.

_____

_____

_____

_____

_____

Blessings I received today

_____

_____

_____

_____

_____

All hard work brings a profit, but mere talk leads only to poverty.
Proverbs 14:23

My TALK with God today

Day

Date

☐ Morning Prayer	☐ Evening Prayer	Choose one or more

ASK

Three Things I am **THANKFUL** for Today:

1.

2.

3.

What do I need forgiveness for?

LET go and let God handle it

Ask God to help with this challenge today.

I set these intentions for the day:

_____

_____

_____

_____

_____

_____

People to keep in my prayers today.

KEEP communicating with God today

A kind deed done today.

Blessings I received today

_____ _____

_____ _____

_____ _____

_____ _____

_____ _____

Jesus Christ is the same yesterday and today and forever.
Hebrews 13:8

My TALK with God today	Day	Date

☐ Morning Prayer	☐ Evening Prayer	Choose one or more

ASK

Three Things I am **THANKFUL** for Today:

1.

2.

3.

What do I need forgiveness for?

LET go and let God handle it

Ask God to help with this challenge today.

I set these intentions for the day:

_____

_____

_____

_____

_____

_____

People to keep in my prayers today.

KEEP communicating with God today

A kind deed done today.	Blessings I received today

_____   _____

_____   _____

_____   _____

_____   _____

_____   _____

Those who know your name trust in you, for you, Lord, have never forsaken those who seek you.
Psalms 9:10

My TALK with God today **Day** **Date**

☐ Morning Prayer	☐ Evening Prayer	Choose one or more	ASK

Three Things I am THANKFUL for Today:

1.

2.

3.

What do I need forgiveness for?

LET go and let God handle it

Ask God to help with this challenge today.

I set these intentions for the day:

_____

_____

_____

_____

_____

_____

People to keep in my prayers today.

KEEP communicating with God today

A kind deed done today.

_____

_____

_____

_____

Blessings I received today

_____

_____

_____

_____

The way of the Lord is a refuge for the blameless, but it is the ruin of those who do evil.
Proverbs 10:29

My TALK with God today

☐ Morning Prayer	☐ Evening Prayer	Choose one or more

ASK

What do I need forgiveness for?

Three Things I am **THANKFUL** for Today:

1.

2.

3.

LET go and let God handle it

Ask God to help with this challenge today.

I set these intentions for the day:

_____

_____

_____

_____

_____

_____

People to keep in my prayers today.

KEEP communicating with God today

A kind deed done today.

_____

_____

_____

_____

Blessings I received today

_____

_____

_____

_____

We are witnesses of these things, and so is the Holy Spirit, whom God has given to those who obey him. Acts 5:32

My TALK with God today   Day   Date

☐ Morning Prayer	☐ Evening Prayer	Choose one or more	**ASK**

Three Things I am **THANKFUL** for Today:

1.

2.

3.

LET go and let God handle it

What do I need forgiveness for?

Ask God to help with this challenge today.

I set these intentions for the day:

_____

_____

_____

_____

_____

_____

People to keep in my prayers today.

KEEP communicating with God today

A kind deed done today.

_____

_____

_____

_____

_____

Blessings I received today

_____

_____

_____

_____

_____

Produce fruit in keeping with repentance. Matthew 3:8

My TALK with God today	Day		Date

ASK

☐ Morning Prayer	☐ Evening Prayer	Choose one or more

What do I need forgiveness for?

Three Things I am **THANKFUL** for Today:

1.

2.

3.

LET go and let God handle it

Ask God to help with this challenge today.

I set these intentions for the day:

_____

_____

_____

_____

_____

_____

People to keep in my prayers today.

KEEP communicating with God today

A kind deed done today.	Blessings I received today
_____	_____
_____	_____
_____	_____
_____	_____
_____	_____

Let us, therefore, make every effort to enter that rest, so that no one will perish by following their example of disobedience. Hebrews 4:11

My TALK with God today

Day　　　　　　　　**Date**

☐ Morning Prayer	☐ Evening Prayer	Choose one or more

Three Things I am **THANKFUL** for Today:

1.

2.

3.

LET go and let God handle it

I set these intentions for the day:

_____

_____

_____

_____

_____

_____

KEEP communicating with God today

A kind deed done today.

_____

_____

_____

_____

_____

Blessings I received today

_____

_____

_____

_____

_____

ASK

What do I need forgiveness for?

Ask God to help with this challenge today.

People to keep in my prayers today.

He gives strength to the weary and increases the power of the weak.
Isaiah 40:29

My TALK with God today | **Day** | **Date**

☐ Morning Prayer	☐ Evening Prayer	Choose one or more

ASK

Three Things I am **THANKFUL** for Today:

1.

2.

3.

What do I need forgiveness for?

LET go and let God handle it

Ask God to help with this challenge today.

I set these intentions for the day:

_____

_____

_____

_____

_____

_____

People to keep in my prayers today.

KEEP communicating with God today

A kind deed done today. | Blessings I received today

_____ | _____

_____ | _____

_____ | _____

_____ | _____

_____ | _____

Remember all the commands of the Lord, that you may obey them and not prostitute yourselves by chasing after the lusts of your own hearts and eyes.
Numbers 15:39

My TALK with God today

Day

Date

☐ Morning Prayer

☐ Evening Prayer

Choose one or more

ASK

Three Things I am **THANKFUL** for Today:

1.

2.

3.

What do I need forgiveness for?

LET go and let God handle it

Ask God to help with this challenge today.

I set these intentions for the day:

_____

_____

_____

_____

_____

_____

People to keep in my prayers today.

KEEP communicating with God today

A kind deed done today.

_____

_____

_____

_____

_____

Blessings I received today

_____

_____

_____

_____

_____

Truly my soul finds rest in God; my salvation comes from him.
Psalms 62:1

My TALK with God today

Day

Date

☐	Morning Prayer	☐	Evening Prayer	Choose one or more

ASK

Three Things I am **THANKFUL** for Today:

What do I need forgiveness for?

1.

2.

3.

LET go and let God handle it

Ask God to help with this challenge today.

I set these intentions for the day:

_____

_____

_____

People to keep in my prayers today.

_____

_____

_____

KEEP communicating with God today

A kind deed done today.

Blessings I received today

_____ _____

_____ _____

_____ _____

_____ _____

_____ _____

Honor the Lord with your wealth, with the firstfruits of all your crops.
Proverbs 3:9

My TALK with God today	**Day**	**Date**

☐ Morning Prayer	☐ Evening Prayer	Choose one or more	**ASK**

Three Things I am **THANKFUL** for Today:

1.

2.

3.

LET go and let God handle it

What do I need forgiveness for?

Ask God to help with this challenge today.

I set these intentions for the day:

_____

_____

_____

_____

_____

_____

People to keep in my prayers today.

KEEP communicating with God today

A kind deed done today.

_____

_____

_____

_____

_____

Blessings I received today

_____

_____

_____

_____

_____

He who supplies seed to the sower and bread for food will also supply and increase your store of seed and will enlarge the harvest of your righteousness.
2 Corinthians 9:10

My TALK with God today

Day

Date

☐ **Morning Prayer**   ☐ **Evening Prayer**   Choose one or more

ASK

What do I need forgiveness for?

Three Things I am **THANKFUL** for Today:

1.

2.

3.

LET go and let God handle it

Ask God to help with this challenge today.

I set these intentions for the day:

_____

_____

_____

_____

_____

_____

People to keep in my prayers today.

KEEP communicating with God today

A kind deed done today.   **Blessings I received today**

_____   _____

_____   _____

_____   _____

_____   _____

_____   _____

My salvation and my honor depend on God; he is my mighty rock, my refuge.
Psalms 62:7

My TALK with God today | **Day** | **Date**

☐ Morning Prayer	☐ Evening Prayer	Choose one or more

ASK

Three Things I am **THANKFUL** for Today:

1.

2.

3.

LET go and let God handle it

What do I need forgiveness for?

Ask God to help with this challenge today.

I set these intentions for the day:

_____

_____

_____

_____

_____

_____

People to keep in my prayers today.

KEEP communicating with God today

A kind deed done today. | Blessings I received today

_____ _____

_____ _____

_____ _____

_____ _____

_____ _____

For whoever wants to save their life will lose it, but whoever loses their life for me will find it.
Matthew 16:25

My TALK with God today → **Day** **Date**

☐ Morning Prayer	☐ Evening Prayer	Choose one or more

ASK

Three Things I am **THANKFUL** for Today:

What do I need forgiveness for?

1.

2.

3.

LET go and let God handle it

Ask God to help with this challenge today.

I set these intentions for the day:

_____

_____

_____

_____

_____

_____

People to keep in my prayers today.

KEEP communicating with God today

A kind deed done today.

_____

_____

_____

_____

_____

Blessings I received today

_____

_____

_____

_____

_____

He will not let your foot slip— he who watches over you will not slumber.
Psalms 121:3

My TALK with God today

Day   **Date**

☐ Morning Prayer	☐ Evening Prayer	Choose one or more

ASK

What do I need forgiveness for?

Three Things I am **THANKFUL** for Today:

1.

2.

3.

LET go and let God handle it

Ask God to help with this challenge today.

I set these intentions for the day:

_____

_____

_____

_____

_____

_____

People to keep in my prayers today.

KEEP communicating with God today

A kind deed done today.

_____

_____

_____

_____

_____

Blessings I received today

_____

_____

_____

_____

_____

Keep his decrees and commands, which I am giving you today, so that it may go well with you and your children after you and that you may live long in the land the Lord your God gives you for all time.
Deuteronomy 4:40

My TALK with God today → **Day** **Date**

☐ Morning Prayer	☐ Evening Prayer	Choose one or more

ASK

Three Things I am **THANKFUL** for Today:

1.

2.

3.

What do I need forgiveness for?

LET go and let God handle it

Ask God to help with this challenge today.

I set these intentions for the day:

_____

_____

_____

_____

_____

_____

People to keep in my prayers today.

KEEP communicating with God today

A kind deed done today.   Blessings I received today

_____   _____

_____   _____

_____   _____

_____   _____

_____   _____

Do not let your hearts be troubled. You believe in God; believe also in me.
John 14:1

My TALK with God today | **Day** | **Date**

☐ Morning Prayer	☐ Evening Prayer	Choose one or more	**ASK**

Three Things I am **THANKFUL** for Today:

1.

2.

3.

LET go and let God handle it

I set these intentions for the day:

_____

_____

_____

_____

_____

_____

KEEP communicating with God today

A kind deed done today.

_____

_____

_____

_____

_____

Blessings I received today

_____

_____

_____

_____

_____

What do I need forgiveness for?

Ask God to help with this challenge today.

People to keep in my prayers today.

Do not be anxious about anything, but in every situation, by prayer and petition, with thanksgiving, present your requests to God. And the peace of God, which transcends all understanding, will guard your hearts and your minds in Christ Jesus.
Philippians 4:6-7

My TALK with God today

Day

Date

☐ Morning Prayer

☐ Evening Prayer

Choose one or more

ASK

Three Things I am **THANKFUL** for Today:

1.

2.

3.

What do I need forgiveness for?

LET go and let God handle it

Ask God to help with this challenge today.

I set these intentions for the day:

_____

_____

_____

_____

_____

People to keep in my prayers today.

KEEP communicating with God today

A kind deed done today.

_____

_____

_____

_____

_____

Blessings I received today

_____

_____

_____

_____

_____

We have come to share in Christ, if indeed we hold our original conviction firmly to the very end.
Hebrews 3:14

My TALK with God today

Day **Date**

☐ Morning Prayer	☐ Evening Prayer	Choose one or more

ASK

Three Things I am **THANKFUL** for Today:

1.

2.

3.

What do I need forgiveness for?

LET go and let God handle it

Ask God to help with this challenge today.

I set these intentions for the day:

_____
_____
_____
_____
_____
_____

People to keep in my prayers today.

KEEP communicating with God today

A kind deed done today.

_____
_____
_____
_____
_____

Blessings I received today

_____
_____
_____
_____
_____

Mercy, peace and love
be yours in
abundance.
Jude 1:2

My TALK with God today **Day** **Date**

☐ Morning Prayer	☐ Evening Prayer	Choose one or more	**ASK**

Three Things I am **THANKFUL** for Today:

1.

2.

3.

LET go and let God handle it

What do I need forgiveness for?

Ask God to help with this challenge today.

I set these intentions for the day:

_____

_____

_____

_____

_____

_____

People to keep in my prayers today.

KEEP communicating with God today

A kind deed done today.

_____

_____

_____

_____

_____

Blessings I received today

_____

_____

_____

_____

_____

Great peace have those who love your law, and nothing can make them stumble. Psalms 119:165

My TALK with God today	Day	.	Date

☐ Morning Prayer	☐ Evening Prayer	Choose one or more	**ASK**

Three Things I am **THANKFUL** for Today:

1.

2.

3.

LET go and let God handle it

I set these intentions for the day:

_____

_____

_____

_____

_____

_____

What do I need forgiveness for?

Ask God to help with this challenge today.

People to keep in my prayers today.

KEEP communicating with God today

A kind deed done today.

_____

_____

_____

_____

_____

Blessings I received today

_____

_____

_____

_____

_____

It is to one's honor to avoid strife, but every fool is quick to quarrel.
Proverbs 20:3

My TALK with God today

Day	Date

☐ Morning Prayer	☐ Evening Prayer	Choose one or more

ASK

Three Things I am **THANKFUL** for Today:

1.

2.

3.

LET go and let God handle it

What do I need forgiveness for?

I set these intentions for the day:

_____
_____
_____
_____
_____
_____

Ask God to help with this challenge today.

People to keep in my prayers today.

KEEP communicating with God today

A kind deed done today.	Blessings I received today
_____	_____
_____	_____
_____	_____
_____	_____
_____	_____

Glory to God in the highest heaven, and on earth peace to those on whom his favor rests.
Luke 2:14

My TALK with God today → Day ___ Date ___

☐ Morning Prayer	☐ Evening Prayer	Choose one or more

ASK

Three Things I am **THANKFUL** for Today:
1.
2.
3.

What do I need forgiveness for?

LET go and let God handle it

Ask God to help with this challenge today.

I set these intentions for the day:

_____

_____

_____

_____

_____

_____

People to keep in my prayers today.

KEEP communicating with God today

A kind deed done today.

_____

_____

_____

_____

_____

Blessings I received today

_____

_____

_____

_____

_____

The God of peace will soon crush Satan under your feet. The grace of our Lord Jesus be with you.
Romans 16:20

My TALK with God today

Day

Date

☐ Morning Prayer ☐ Evening Prayer Choose one or more

ASK

Three Things I am **THANKFUL** for Today:

1.

2.

3.

What do I need forgiveness for?

LET go and let God handle it

Ask God to help with this challenge today.

I set these intentions for the day:

_____

_____

_____

_____

_____

_____

People to keep in my prayers today.

KEEP communicating with God today

A kind deed done today.

_____

_____

_____

_____

_____

Blessings I received today

_____

_____

_____

_____

_____

Salvation is found in no one else, for there is no other name under heaven given to mankind by which we must be saved.
Acts 4:12

My TALK with God today → **Day** | **Date**

☐	Morning Prayer	☐	Evening Prayer	Choose one or more

ASK

Three Things I am **THANKFUL** for Today:

1.

2.

3.

What do I need forgiveness for?

LET go and let God handle it

Ask God to help with this challenge today.

I set these intentions for the day:

_____

_____

_____

_____

_____

_____

People to keep in my prayers today.

KEEP communicating with God today

A kind deed done today.   **Blessings I received today**

_____   _____

_____   _____

_____   _____

_____   _____

_____   _____

Be completely humble and gentle; be patient, bearing with one another in love.
Ephesians 4:2

My TALK with God today

Day	Date

☐ Morning Prayer	☐ Evening Prayer	Choose one or more

ASK

Three Things I am **THANKFUL** for Today:	**What do I need forgiveness for?**

1.

2.

3.

LET go and let God handle it

Ask God to help with this challenge today.

I set these intentions for the day:

_____

_____

_____

_____

_____

_____

People to keep in my prayers today.

KEEP communicating with God today

A kind deed done today.	Blessings I received today
_____	_____
_____	_____
_____	_____
_____	_____
_____	_____

Let us not become weary in doing good, for at the proper time we will reap a harvest if we do not give up.
Galatians 6:9

My TALK with God today

Day _____ **Date** _____

☐ Morning Prayer	☐ Evening Prayer	Choose one or more

ASK

Three Things I am **THANKFUL** for Today:

1. _____

2. _____

3. _____

What do I need forgiveness for?

LET go and let God handle it

Ask God to help with this challenge today.

I set these intentions for the day:

_____

_____

_____

_____

_____

_____

People to keep in my prayers today.

KEEP communicating with God today

A kind deed done today.

_____

_____

_____

_____

_____

Blessings I received today

_____

_____

_____

_____

_____

A gift opens the way and ushers the giver into the presence of the great.
Proverbs 18:16

My TALK with God today → **Day** _____ **Date** _____

❑ Morning Prayer	❑ Evening Prayer	Choose one or more

ASK

Three Things I am **THANKFUL** for Today:
1.
2.
3.

What do I need forgiveness for?

LET go and let God handle it

Ask God to help with this challenge today.

I set these intentions for the day:
_____
_____
_____
_____
_____
_____

People to keep in my prayers today.

KEEP communicating with God today

A kind deed done today.
_____
_____
_____
_____
_____

Blessings I received today
_____
_____
_____
_____
_____

The Lord is compassionate and gracious, slow to anger, abounding in love.
Psalms 103:8

My TALK with God today → **Day**   **Date**

☐	Morning Prayer	☐	Evening Prayer	Choose one or more

ASK

Three Things I am **THANKFUL** for Today:

1.

2.

3.

What do I need forgiveness for?

LET go and let God handle it

Ask God to help with this challenge today.

I set these intentions for the day:

_____

_____

_____

_____

_____

People to keep in my prayers today.

KEEP communicating with God today

A kind deed done today.   Blessings I received today

_____   _____

_____   _____

_____   _____

_____   _____

_____   _____

The one who stands firm to the end will be saved. Matthew 24:13

My TALK with God today

| Day | Date |

| ☐ Morning Prayer | ☐ Evening Prayer | Choose one or more |

ASK

Three Things I am **THANKFUL** for Today:

1.

2.

3.

What do I need forgiveness for?

LET go and let God handle it

Ask God to help with this challenge today.

I set these intentions for the day:

_____

_____

_____

_____

_____

_____

People to keep in my prayers today.

KEEP communicating with God today

| A kind deed done today. | Blessings I received today |

_____ _____

_____ _____

_____ _____

_____ _____

_____ _____

Godliness with contentment is great gain.
1 Timothy 6:6

My TALK with God today	Day	Date

☐ Morning Prayer	☐ Evening Prayer	Choose one or more	ASK

Three Things I am **THANKFUL** for Today:

1.

2.

3.

What do I need forgiveness for?

LET go and let God handle it

Ask God to help with this challenge today.

I set these intentions for the day:

_____

_____

_____

_____

_____

_____

People to keep in my prayers today.

KEEP communicating with God today

A kind deed done today.

_____

_____

_____

_____

_____

Blessings I received today

_____

_____

_____

_____

_____

Better a little with righteousness than much gain with injustice.
Proverbs 16:8

My TALK with God today ➔ **Day**   **Date**

☐ Morning Prayer	☐ Evening Prayer	Choose one or more

ASK

Three Things I am **THANKFUL** for Today:
1.
2.
3.

What do I need forgiveness for?

LET go and let God handle it

Ask God to help with this challenge today.

I set these intentions for the day:

_____

_____

_____

_____

_____

_____

People to keep in my prayers today.

KEEP communicating with God today

A kind deed done today.

_____

_____

_____

_____

_____

Blessings I received today

_____

_____

_____

_____

_____

Take delight in the Lord, and he will give you the desires of your heart.
Psalms 37:4

My TALK with God today → Day

Date

☐ Morning Prayer	☐ Evening Prayer	Choose one or more

ASK

Three Things I am THANKFUL for Today:

1.

2.

3.

What do I need forgiveness for?

LET go and let God handle it

Ask God to help with this challenge today.

I set these intentions for the day:

_____

_____

_____

_____

_____

_____

People to keep in my prayers today.

KEEP communicating with God today

A kind deed done today.

Blessings I received today

_____   _____

_____   _____

_____   _____

_____   _____

_____   _____

Let your gentleness be evident to all.
The Lord is near.
Philippians 4:5

My TALK with God today → **Day**   **Date**

☐ Morning Prayer	☐ Evening Prayer	Choose one or more

ASK

Three Things I am THANKFUL for Today:

1.

2.

3.

What do I need forgiveness for?

LET go and let God handle it

Ask God to help with this challenge today.

I set these intentions for the day:

_____

_____

_____

_____

_____

_____

People to keep in my prayers today.

KEEP communicating with God today

A kind deed done today.

_____

_____

_____

_____

_____

Blessings I received today

_____

_____

_____

_____

_____

All day long he craves for more, but the righteous give without sparing.
Proverbs 21:26

My TALK with God today   **Day**   **Date**

☐	Morning Prayer	☐	Evening Prayer	Choose one or more

ASK

Three Things I am **THANKFUL** for Today:

1.

2.

3.

What do I need forgiveness for?

LET go and let God handle it

Ask God to help with this challenge today.

I set these intentions for the day:

_____

_____

_____

People to keep in my prayers today.

_____

_____

_____

KEEP communicating with God today

A kind deed done today.

_____

_____

_____

_____

_____

Blessings I received today

_____

_____

_____

_____

_____

The wicked borrow and do not repay, but the righteous give generously.
Psalms 37:21

My TALK with God today

Day

Date

| ☐ | Morning Prayer | ☐ | Evening Prayer | Choose one or more |

ASK

Three Things I am **THANKFUL** for Today:

1.

2.

3.

What do I need forgiveness for?

LET go and let God handle it

Ask God to help with this challenge today.

I set these intentions for the day:

_____

_____

_____

_____

_____

_____

People to keep in my prayers today.

KEEP communicating with God today

A kind deed done today.

_____

_____

_____

_____

_____

Blessings I received today

_____

_____

_____

_____

_____

Bless those who persecute you; bless and do not curse.
Romans 12:14

My TALK with God today **Day** **Date**

☐ Morning Prayer	☐ Evening Prayer	Choose one or more

ASK

Three Things I am **THANKFUL** for Today:

1.

2.

3.

What do I need forgiveness for?

LET go and let God handle it

Ask God to help with this challenge today.

I set these intentions for the day:

_____

_____

_____

_____

_____

_____

People to keep in my prayers today.

KEEP communicating with God today

A kind deed done today.

Blessings I received today

_____ _____

_____ _____

_____ _____

_____ _____

_____ _____

The grace of the Lord Jesus Christ be with your spirit.
Philemon 1:25

My TALK with God today | Day | Date

| ☐ Morning Prayer | ☐ Evening Prayer | Choose one or more |

ASK

Three Things I am **THANKFUL** for Today:

1.

2.

3.

What do I need forgiveness for?

LET go and let God handle it

Ask God to help with this challenge today.

I set these intentions for the day:

_____

_____

_____

_____

_____

_____

People to keep in my prayers today.

KEEP communicating with God today

A kind deed done today.

Blessings I received today

_____   _____

_____   _____

_____   _____

_____   _____

_____   _____

Blessed are those who keep his statutes and seek him with all their heart.
Psalms 119:2

My TALK with God today | Day | Date

| ☐ Morning Prayer | ☐ Evening Prayer | Choose one or more |

ASK

Three Things I am **THANKFUL** for Today:

1.

2.

3.

What do I need forgiveness for?

LET go and let God handle it

Ask God to help with this challenge today.

I set these intentions for the day:

_____

_____

_____

_____

_____

People to keep in my prayers today.

KEEP communicating with God today

A kind deed done today.　　Blessings I received today

_____　　_____

_____　　_____

_____　　_____

_____　　_____

_____　　_____

The blessing of the Lord brings wealth, without painful toil for it.
Proverbs 10:22

My TALK with God today

Day

Date

☐ Morning Prayer	☐ Evening Prayer	Choose one or more

ASK

Three Things I am **THANKFUL** for Today:

1.

2.

3.

What do I need forgiveness for?

LET go and let God handle it

Ask God to help with this challenge today.

I set these intentions for the day:

_____

_____

_____

_____

_____

People to keep in my prayers today.

KEEP communicating with God today

A kind deed done today.

_____

_____

_____

_____

Blessings I received today

_____

_____

_____

_____

Let your face shine on your servant; save me in your unfailing love. Psalms 31:16

My TALK with God today → **Day** **Date**

☐ Morning Prayer	☐ Evening Prayer	Choose one or more

ASK

Three Things I am **THANKFUL** for Today:

1.

2.

3.

What do I need forgiveness for?

LET go and let God handle it

Ask God to help with this challenge today.

I set these intentions for the day:

_____

_____

_____

_____

_____

_____

People to keep in my prayers today.

KEEP communicating with God today

A kind deed done today.

_____
_____
_____
_____
_____

Blessings I received today

_____
_____
_____
_____
_____

Praise be to the God and Father of our Lord Jesus Christ, who has blessed us in the heavenly realms with every spiritual blessing in Christ. Ephesians 1:3

My TALK with God today → **Day**   **Date**

☐ Morning Prayer	☐ Evening Prayer	Choose one or more

ASK

Three Things I am **THANKFUL** for Today:

What do I need forgiveness for?

1.

2.

3.

LET go and let God handle it

Ask God to help with this challenge today.

I set these intentions for the day:

_____

_____

_____

People to keep in my prayers today.

_____

_____

_____

_____

KEEP communicating with God today

A kind deed done today.

Blessings I received today

_____ _____

_____ _____

_____ _____

_____ _____

_____ _____

Do everything in love.
1 Corinthians 16:14

My TALK with God today

Day _____ **Date** _____

☐ Morning Prayer	☐ Evening Prayer	Choose one or more

Three Things I am **THANKFUL** for Today:
1.
2.
3.

LET go and let God handle it

I set these intentions for the day:

_____

_____

_____

_____

_____

_____

ASK

What do I need forgiveness for?

Ask God to help with this challenge today.

People to keep in my prayers today.

KEEP communicating with God today

A kind deed done today.

_____

_____

_____

_____

_____

Blessings I received today

_____

_____

_____

_____

_____

Blessings crown the head of the righteous, but violence overwhelms the mouth of the wicked. Proverbs 10:6

My TALK with God today → **Day** **Date**

☐ Morning Prayer	☐ Evening Prayer	Choose one or more

ASK

Three Things I am THANKFUL for Today:

1.

2.

3.

What do I need forgiveness for?

LET go and let God handle it

Ask God to help with this challenge today.

I set these intentions for the day:

_____

_____

_____

_____

_____

_____

People to keep in my prayers today.

KEEP communicating with God today

A kind deed done today.	Blessings I received today
_____	_____
_____	_____
_____	_____
_____	_____

Let the morning bring me word of your unfailing love, for I have put my trust in you. Show me the way I should go, for to you I entrust my life. Psalms 143:8

My TALK with God today

Day

Date

☐ **Morning Prayer**   ☐ **Evening Prayer**   Choose one or more

ASK

Three Things I am **THANKFUL** for Today:

1.

2.

3.

What do I need forgiveness for?

LET go and let God handle it

Ask God to help with this challenge today.

I set these intentions for the day:

_____

_____

_____

_____

_____

_____

People to keep in my prayers today.

KEEP communicating with God today

A kind deed done today.

_____

_____

_____

_____

_____

Blessings I received today

_____

_____

_____

_____

_____

Do not fear, for I am with you; do not be dismayed, for I am your God. I will strengthen you and help you; I will uphold you with my righteous right hand.
Isaiah 41:10

My TALK with God today

Day

Date

☐ Morning Prayer	☐ Evening Prayer	Choose one or more

ASK

Three Things I am **THANKFUL** for Today:

1.

2.

3.

What do I need forgiveness for?

LET go and let God handle it

Ask God to help with this challenge today.

I set these intentions for the day:

_____

_____

_____

People to keep in my prayers today.

_____

_____

_____

KEEP communicating with God today

A kind deed done today.

_____

_____

_____

_____

_____

Blessings I received today

_____

_____

_____

_____

_____

For I know the plans I have for you, declares the Lord, plans to prosper you and not to harm you, plans to give you hope and a future.
Jeremiah 29:11

My TALK with God today | **Day** | **Date**

☐ Morning Prayer	☐ Evening Prayer	Choose one or more

ASK

Three Things I am **THANKFUL** for Today:

1.

2.

3.

LET go and let God handle it

What do I need forgiveness for?

Ask God to help with this challenge today.

I set these intentions for the day:
_____
_____
_____
_____
_____
_____

People to keep in my prayers today.

KEEP communicating with God today

A kind deed done today. | **Blessings I received today**
_____ | _____
_____ | _____
_____ | _____
_____ | _____
_____ | _____

Worship the Lord your God, and his blessing will be on your food and water. I will take away sickness from among you.
Exodus 23:25

My TALK with God today

Day

Date

☐ Morning Prayer	☐ Evening Prayer	Choose one or more

ASK

Three Things I am **THANKFUL** for Today:

1.

2.

3.

LET go and let God handle it

What do I need forgiveness for?

Ask God to help with this challenge today.

I set these intentions for the day:

_____

_____

_____

_____

_____

_____

People to keep in my prayers today.

KEEP communicating with God today

A kind deed done today.	Blessings I received today
_____	_____
_____	_____
_____	_____
_____	_____
_____	_____

Trust in the Lord with all your heart and lean not on your own understanding; in all your ways submit to him, and he will make your paths straight.
Proverbs 3:5-6

My TALK with God today   **Day**   **Date**

☐ Morning Prayer	☐ Evening Prayer	Choose one or more	**ASK**

Three Things I am **THANKFUL** for Today:

1.

2.

3.

What do I need
forgiveness for?

LET go and let God handle it

Ask God to help with this
challenge today.

I set these intentions for the day:

_____

_____

_____

_____

_____

People to keep in my
prayers today.

KEEP communicating with God today

A kind deed done today.   Blessings I received today

_____   _____

_____   _____

_____   _____

_____   _____

_____   _____

Whoever does not
take up their cross
and follow me is not
worthy of me.
Matthew 10:38

My TALK with God today **Day** **Date**

☐ Morning Prayer	☐ Evening Prayer	Choose one or more

ASK

Three Things I am **THANKFUL** for Today:

1.

2.

3.

What do I need forgiveness for?

LET go and let God handle it

Ask God to help with this challenge today.

I set these intentions for the day:

_____

_____

_____

_____

_____

_____

People to keep in my prayers today.

KEEP communicating with God today

A kind deed done today.

_____

_____

_____

_____

_____

Blessings I received today

_____

_____

_____

_____

_____

May he give you the desire of your heart and make all your plans succeed. Psalms 20:4

My TALK with God today   **Day**   **Date**

☐ Morning Prayer	☐ Evening Prayer	Choose one or more

ASK

Three Things I am **THANKFUL** for Today:

1.

2.

3.

What do I need forgiveness for?

LET go and let God handle it

Ask God to help with this challenge today.

I set these intentions for the day:

_____

_____

_____

_____

_____

_____

People to keep in my prayers today.

KEEP communicating with God today

A kind deed done today.   **Blessings I received today**

_____   _____

_____   _____

_____   _____

_____   _____

_____   _____

Over all these virtues put on love, which binds them all together in perfect unity.
Colossians 3:14

My TALK with God today   **Day**   **Date**

| ☐ | Morning Prayer | ☐ | Evening Prayer | Choose one or more | **ASK** |

Three Things I am **THANKFUL** for Today:

1.

2.

3.

What do I need forgiveness for?

LET go and let God handle it

Ask God to help with this challenge today.

I set these intentions for the day:

_____

_____

_____

_____

_____

_____

People to keep in my prayers today.

KEEP communicating with God today

A kind deed done today.

Blessings I received today

_____   _____

_____   _____

_____   _____

_____   _____

Now these three remain: faith, hope and love. But the greatest of these is love.
1 Corinthians 13:13

My TALK with God today	Day		Date

☐ Morning Prayer	☐ Evening Prayer	Choose one or more	ASK

Three Things I am **THANKFUL** for Today:
1.
2.
3.

What do I need forgiveness for?

LET go and let God handle it

Ask God to help with this challenge today.

I set these intentions for the day:

_____

_____

_____

_____

_____

_____

People to keep in my prayers today.

KEEP communicating with God today

A kind deed done today.	Blessings I received today
_____	_____
_____	_____
_____	_____
_____	_____
_____	_____

When you ask, you must believe and not doubt, because the one who doubts is like a wave of the sea, blown and tossed by the wind.
Romans 8:26

My TALK with God today

Day

Date

☐	Morning Prayer	☐	Evening Prayer	Choose one or more

ASK

Three Things I am **THANKFUL** for Today:

1.

2.

3.

What do I need forgiveness for?

LET go and let God handle it

Ask God to help with this challenge today.

I set these intentions for the day:

_____

_____

_____

_____

_____

_____

People to keep in my prayers today.

KEEP communicating with God today

A kind deed done today.

_____

_____

_____

_____

_____

Blessings I received today

_____

_____

_____

_____

_____

You are all children of God through faith, for all of you who were baptized into Christ have clothed yourselves with Christ. Galatians 3:26-27

My TALK with God today

Day

Date

| ☐ Morning Prayer | ☐ Evening Prayer | Choose one or more | ASK |

Three Things I am **THANKFUL** for Today:

1.

2.

3.

What do I need forgiveness for?

LET go and let God handle it

Ask God to help with this challenge today.

I set these intentions for the day:

_____

_____

_____

_____

_____

_____

People to keep in my prayers today.

KEEP communicating with God today

A kind deed done today.

_____

_____

_____

_____

_____

Blessings I received today

_____

_____

_____

_____

_____

How good and pleasant it is when God's people live together in unity! Psalms 133:1

My TALK with God today | **Day** | **Date**

☐ Morning Prayer	☐ Evening Prayer	Choose one or more

Three Things I am **THANKFUL** for Today:

1.

2.

3.

LET go and let God handle it

What do I need forgiveness for?

Ask God to help with this challenge today.

I set these intentions for the day:

_____

_____

_____

_____

_____

_____

People to keep in my prayers today.

KEEP communicating with God today

A kind deed done today. | **Blessings I received today**

_____ _____

_____ _____

_____ _____

_____ _____

_____ _____

Come to me, all you who are weary and burdened, and I will give you rest.
Matthew 11:28

My TALK with God today → **Day**   **Date**

☐ Morning Prayer	☐ Evening Prayer	Choose one or more

ASK

Three Things I am **THANKFUL** for Today:

1.

2.

3.

LET go and let God handle it

What do I need forgiveness for?

Ask God to help with this challenge today.

I set these intentions for the day:

_____

_____

_____

_____

_____

_____

People to keep in my prayers today.

KEEP communicating with God today

A kind deed done today.   **Blessings I received today**

_____   _____

_____   _____

_____   _____

_____   _____

_____   _____

The fruit of the Spirit is love, joy, peace, forbearance, kindness, goodness, faithfulness, gentleness and self-control. Against such things there is no law. Galatians 5:22-23

My TALK with God today **Day** **Date**

☐ Morning Prayer	☐ Evening Prayer	Choose one or more

ASK

Three Things I am **THANKFUL** for Today:

1.

2.

3.

What do I need forgiveness for?

LET go and let God handle it

Ask God to help with this challenge today.

I set these intentions for the day:

_____
_____
_____
_____
_____

People to keep in my prayers today.

KEEP communicating with God today

A kind deed done today.

Blessings I received today

_____ _____
_____ _____
_____ _____
_____ _____
_____ _____

For the Lord gives wisdom; from his mouth come knowledge and understanding. Proverbs 2:6

My TALK with God today → Day ___ Date ___

☐ Morning Prayer	☐ Evening Prayer	Choose one or more

ASK

Three Things I am **THANKFUL** for Today:

1.

2.

3.

What do I need forgiveness for?

LET go and let God handle it

Ask God to help with this challenge today.

I set these intentions for the day:

_____

_____

_____

_____

_____

People to keep in my prayers today.

KEEP communicating with God today

A kind deed done today.

_____

_____

_____

_____

_____

Blessings I received today

_____

_____

_____

_____

_____

Let us then approach God's throne of grace with confidence, so that we may receive mercy and find grace to help us in our time of need.
Hebrews 4:16

My TALK with God today → **Day** **Date**

☐ Morning Prayer	☐ Evening Prayer	Choose one or more

ASK

Three Things I am THANKFUL for Today:

1.

2.

3.

What do I need forgiveness for?

LET go and let God handle it

Ask God to help with this challenge today.

I set these intentions for the day:

_____

_____

_____

_____

_____

_____

People to keep in my prayers today.

KEEP communicating with God today

A kind deed done today.   **Blessings I received today**

_____   _____

_____   _____

_____   _____

_____   _____

May the God of hope fill you with all joy and peace as you trust in him, so that you may overflow with hope by the power of the Holy Spirit.
Romans 15:13

My TALK with God today

Day

Date

☐ Morning Prayer ☐ Evening Prayer | Choose one or more

ASK

Three Things I am **THANKFUL** for Today:

1.

2.

3.

What do I need forgiveness for?

LET go and let God handle it

Ask God to help with this challenge today.

I set these intentions for the day:

_____

_____

_____

_____

_____

_____

People to keep in my prayers today.

KEEP communicating with God today

A kind deed done today.

_____

_____

_____

_____

_____

Blessings I received today

_____

_____

_____

_____

_____

Let us hold unswervingly to the hope we profess, for he who promised is faithful.
Hebrews 10:23

My TALK with God today

Day	Date

☐ Morning Prayer	☐ Evening Prayer	Choose one or more

ASK

Three Things I am **THANKFUL** for Today:

1.

2.

3.

What do I need forgiveness for?

LET go and let God handle it

Ask God to help with this challenge today.

I set these intentions for the day:

_____

_____

_____

_____

_____

_____

People to keep in my prayers today.

KEEP communicating with God today

A kind deed done today.

_____

_____

_____

_____

_____

Blessings I received today

_____

_____

_____

_____

_____

There is one body and one Spirit, just as you were called to one hope when you were called. Ephesians 4:4

My TALK with God today

Day | **Date**

☐ Morning Prayer | ☐ Evening Prayer | Choose one or more

Three Things I am **THANKFUL** for Today:

1.

2.

3.

LET go and let God handle it

I set these intentions for the day:

_____

_____

_____

_____

_____

ASK

What do I need forgiveness for?

Ask God to help with this challenge today.

People to keep in my prayers today.

KEEP communicating with God today

A kind deed done today.

_____

_____

_____

_____

_____

Blessings I received today

_____

_____

_____

_____

_____

Direct my footsteps according to your word; let no sin rule over me.
Psalms 119:133

My TALK with God today **Day** **Date**

☐ Morning Prayer	☐ Evening Prayer	Choose one or more

ASK

Three Things I am **THANKFUL** for Today:

1.

2.

3.

What do I need forgiveness for?

LET go and let God handle it

Ask God to help with this challenge today.

I set these intentions for the day:

_____

_____

_____

_____

_____

_____

People to keep in my prayers today.

KEEP communicating with God today

A kind deed done today.

_____

_____

_____

_____

_____

Blessings I received today

_____

_____

_____

_____

_____

Blessed are those who find wisdom, those who gain understanding.
Proverbs 3:13

My TALK with God today | **Day** | **Date**

☐	Morning Prayer	☐	Evening Prayer	Choose one or more

ASK

Three Things I am **THANKFUL** for Today:
1.
2.
3.

What do I need forgiveness for?

LET go and let God handle it

Ask God to help with this challenge today.

I set these intentions for the day:
_____
_____
_____
_____
_____
_____

People to keep in my prayers today.

KEEP communicating with God today

A kind deed done today.	Blessings I received today
_____	_____
_____	_____
_____	_____
_____	_____
_____	_____

Whoever serves me must follow me; and where I am, my servant also will be. My Father will honor the one who serves me.
John 12:26

My TALK with God today → **Day** **Date**

☐ **Morning Prayer**	☐ **Evening Prayer**	Choose one or more

ASK

Three Things I am **THANKFUL** for Today:
1.
2.
3.

What do I need forgiveness for?

LET go and let God handle it

Ask God to help with this challenge today.

I set these intentions for the day:

_____

_____

_____

_____

_____

People to keep in my prayers today.

KEEP communicating with God today

A kind deed done today.	**Blessings I received today**
_____	_____
_____	_____
_____	_____
_____	_____
_____	_____

No one can serve two masters. Either you will hate the one and love the other, or you will be devoted to the one and despise the other. You cannot serve both God and money.
Matthew 6:24

My TALK with God today	Day	Date

☐ Morning Prayer	☐ Evening Prayer	Choose one or more	ASK

Three Things I am **THANKFUL** for Today:

1.

2.

3.

LET go and let God handle it

ASK

What do I need forgiveness for?

Ask God to help with this challenge today.

I set these intentions for the day:

_____
_____
_____
_____
_____

People to keep in my prayers today.

KEEP communicating with God today

A kind deed done today.

_____
_____
_____
_____
_____

Blessings I received today

_____
_____
_____
_____
_____

For we are co-workers in God's service; you are God's field, God's building.
1 Corinthians 3:9

My TALK with God today → **Day**   **Date**

☐	Morning Prayer	☐	Evening Prayer	Choose one or more

ASK

Three Things I am **THANKFUL** for Today:
1.
2.
3.

What do I need forgiveness for?

LET go and let God handle it

Ask God to help with this challenge today.

I set these intentions for the day:

_____

_____

_____

_____

_____

_____

People to keep in my prayers today.

KEEP communicating with God today

A kind deed done today.	Blessings I received today
_____	_____
_____	_____
_____	_____
_____	_____
_____	_____

God is not unjust; he will not forget your work and the love you have shown him as you have helped his people and continue to help them.
Hebrews 6:10

My TALK with God today → Day

Date

☐ Morning Prayer	☐ Evening Prayer	Choose one or more

ASK

Three Things I am THANKFUL for Today:

1.

2.

3.

LET go and let God handle it

What do I need forgiveness for?

Ask God to help with this challenge today.

I set these intentions for the day:

_____

_____

_____

_____

_____

_____

People to keep in my prayers today.

KEEP communicating with God today

A kind deed done today.

_____

_____

_____

_____

_____

Blessings I received today

_____

_____

_____

_____

_____

I will hasten and not delay to obey your commands.
Psalms 119:60

My TALK with God today → **Day** **Date**

☐ Morning Prayer	☐ Evening Prayer	Choose one or more

ASK

Three Things I am **THANKFUL** for Today:

1.

2.

3.

What do I need forgiveness for?

LET go and let God handle it

Ask God to help with this challenge today.

I set these intentions for the day:

_____

_____

_____

_____

_____

_____

People to keep in my prayers today.

KEEP communicating with God today

A kind deed done today.	Blessings I received today
_____	_____
_____	_____
_____	_____
_____	_____
_____	_____

Consequently, faith comes from hearing the message, and the message is heard through the word about Christ. Romans 10:17

My TALK with God today	Day	Date

☐ Morning Prayer	☐ Evening Prayer	Choose one or more	ASK

Three Things I am **THANKFUL** for Today:

1.

2.

3.

What do I need forgiveness for?

LET go and let God handle it

Ask God to help with this challenge today.

I set these intentions for the day:

_____

_____

_____

_____

_____

_____

_____

People to keep in my prayers today.

KEEP communicating with God today

A kind deed done today.

_____

_____

_____

_____

_____

Blessings I received today

_____

_____

_____

_____

_____

Whatever you have learned or received or heard from me, or seen in me—put it into practice. And the God of peace will be with you.
Philippians 4:9

My TALK with God today

Day	Date

☐ Morning Prayer	☐ Evening Prayer	Choose one or more

ASK

Three Things I am **THANKFUL** for Today:

1.

2.

3.

What do I need forgiveness for?

LET go and let God handle it

Ask God to help with this challenge today.

I set these intentions for the day:

_____

_____

_____

_____

_____

_____

People to keep in my prayers today.

KEEP communicating with God today

A kind deed done today.

_____

_____

_____

_____

_____

Blessings I received today

_____

_____

_____

_____

_____

The fear of the Lord is the beginning of knowledge, but fools despise wisdom and instruction.
Proverbs 1:7

My TALK with God today   **Day**   **Date**

☐ Morning Prayer	☐ Evening Prayer	Choose one or more	**ASK**

Three Things I am **THANKFUL** for Today:

1.

2.

3.

What do I need forgiveness for?

LET go and let God handle it

Ask God to help with this challenge today.

I set these intentions for the day:

_____

_____

_____

People to keep in my prayers today.

_____

_____

_____

KEEP communicating with God today

A kind deed done today.   **Blessings I received today**

_____   _____

_____   _____

_____   _____

_____   _____

_____   _____

Let the message of Christ dwell among you richly as you teach and admonish one another with all wisdom through psalms, hymns, and songs from the Spirit, singing to God with gratitude
in your hearts.
Colossians 3:16

My TALK with God today → **Day** **Date**

☐	Morning Prayer	☐	Evening Prayer	Choose one or more

ASK

Three Things I am **THANKFUL** for Today:

What do I need forgiveness for?

1.

2.

3.

LET go and let God handle it

Ask God to help with this challenge today.

I set these intentions for the day:

_____

_____

_____

_____

_____

People to keep in my prayers today.

KEEP communicating with God today

A kind deed done today.   **Blessings I received today**

_____   _____

_____   _____

_____   _____

_____   _____

_____   _____

Therefore anyone who sets aside one of the least of these commands and teaches others accordingly will be called least in the kingdom of heaven, but whoever practices and teaches these commands will be called great in the kingdom of heaven.
Matthew 5:19

My TALK with God today	**Day**	**Date**

☐ Morning Prayer	☐ Evening Prayer	Choose one or more

ASK

Three Things I am **THANKFUL** for Today:
1.
2.
3.

What do I need forgiveness for?

LET go and let God handle it

Ask God to help with this challenge today.

I set these intentions for the day:

_____

_____

_____

_____

_____

People to keep in my prayers today.

KEEP communicating with God today

A kind deed done today.	Blessings I received today
_____	_____
_____	_____
_____	_____
_____	_____
_____	_____

I will instruct you and teach you in the way you should go; I will counsel you with my loving eye on you.
Psalms 32:8

My TALK with God today

Day

Date

☐ Morning Prayer	☐ Evening Prayer	Choose one or more

ASK

Three Things I am **THANKFUL** for Today:

1.

2.

3.

What do I need forgiveness for?

LET go and let God handle it

Ask God to help with this challenge today.

I set these intentions for the day:

_____

_____

_____

_____

_____

People to keep in my prayers today.

KEEP communicating with God today

A kind deed done today.	Blessings I received today
_____	_____
_____	_____
_____	_____
_____	_____
_____	_____

By this everyone will know that you are my disciples, if you love one another.
John 13:35

My TALK with God today ➤ **Day**   **Date**

☐ Morning Prayer	☐ Evening Prayer	Choose one or more

Three Things I am **THANKFUL** for Today:

1.

2.

3.

What do I need forgiveness for?

LET go and let God handle it

Ask God to help with this challenge today.

I set these intentions for the day:

_____

_____

_____

_____

_____

_____

People to keep in my prayers today.

KEEP communicating with God today

A kind deed done today.   Blessings I received today

_____   _____

_____   _____

_____   _____

_____   _____

_____   _____

Whoever gives heed to instruction prospers, and blessed is the one who trusts in the Lord.
Proverbs 16:20

My TALK with God today → **Day** | **Date**

☐ Morning Prayer	☐ Evening Prayer	Choose one or more

ASK

Three Things I am **THANKFUL** for Today:

1.

2.

3.

What do I need forgiveness for?

LET go and let God handle it

Ask God to help with this challenge today.

I set these intentions for the day:

_____

_____

_____

_____

_____

_____

People to keep in my prayers today.

KEEP communicating with God today

A kind deed done today.

_____

_____

_____

_____

_____

Blessings I received today

_____

_____

_____

_____

_____

Preach the word; be prepared in season and out of season; correct, rebuke and encourage—with great patience and careful instruction.
2 Timothy 4:2

My TALK with God today

Day   **Date**

☐ Morning Prayer   ☐ Evening Prayer   Choose one or more

ASK

Three Things I am **THANKFUL** for Today:

1.

2.

3.

What do I need forgiveness for?

LET go and let God handle it

Ask God to help with this challenge today.

I set these intentions for the day:

_____

_____

_____

_____

_____

_____

People to keep in my prayers today.

KEEP communicating with God today

A kind deed done today.   Blessings I received today

_____   _____

_____   _____

_____   _____

_____   _____

_____   _____

Therefore he is able to save completely those who come to God through him, because he always lives to intercede for them.
Hebrews 7:25

My TALK with God today

☐ Morning Prayer	☐ Evening Prayer	Choose one or more

ASK

Three Things I am **THANKFUL** for Today:

1.

2.

3.

What do I need forgiveness for?

LET go and let God handle it

Ask God to help with this challenge today.

I set these intentions for the day:

_____

_____

_____

_____

_____

_____

People to keep in my prayers today.

KEEP communicating with God today

A kind deed done today.

Blessings I received today

_____   _____

_____   _____

_____   _____

_____   _____

_____   _____

Consider that our present sufferings are not worth comparing with the glory that will be revealed in us.
Romans 8:18

My TALK with God today

Day

Date

☐ **Morning Prayer** ☐ **Evening Prayer** Choose one or more

ASK

What do I need forgiveness for?

Three Things I am THANKFUL for Today:

1.

2.

3.

LET go and let God handle it

Ask God to help with this challenge today.

I set these intentions for the day:

_____

_____

_____

_____

_____

_____

People to keep in my prayers today.

KEEP communicating with God today

A kind deed done today.

_____

_____

_____

_____

_____

Blessings I received today

_____

_____

_____

_____

_____

From the Lord comes deliverance. May your blessing be on your people.
Psalms 3:8

My TALK with God today → **Day** **Date**

☐ Morning Prayer	☐ Evening Prayer	Choose one or more

ASK

Three Things I am **THANKFUL** for Today:

1.

2.

3.

What do I need forgiveness for?

LET go and let God handle it

Ask God to help with this challenge today.

I set these intentions for the day:

_____

_____

_____

_____

_____

_____

People to keep in my prayers today.

KEEP communicating with God today

A kind deed done today.

_____

_____

_____

_____

_____

Blessings I received today

_____

_____

_____

_____

_____

Heal me, Lord, and I will be healed; save me and I will be saved, for you are the one I praise.
Jeremiah 17:14

My TALK with God today | **Day** | **Date**

☐ Morning Prayer	☐ Evening Prayer	Choose one or more

ASK

Three Things I am THANKFUL for Today:

1.

2.

3.

What do I need forgiveness for?

LET go and let God handle it

Ask God to help with this challenge today.

I set these intentions for the day:

_____

_____

_____

_____

_____

_____

People to keep in my prayers today.

KEEP communicating with God today

A kind deed done today.

_____

_____

_____

_____

_____

Blessings I received today

_____

_____

_____

_____

_____

Keep your father's command and do not forsake your mother's teaching. Proverbs 6:20

My TALK with God today | **Day** | **Date**

☐ Morning Prayer	☐ Evening Prayer	Choose one or more

ASK

Three Things I am **THANKFUL** for Today:

1.

2.

3.

What do I need forgiveness for?

LET go and let God handle it

Ask God to help with this challenge today.

I set these intentions for the day:

_____

_____

_____

_____

_____

_____

People to keep in my prayers today.

KEEP communicating with God today

A kind deed done today. | Blessings I received today

_____ | _____

_____ | _____

_____ | _____

_____ | _____

_____ | _____

Teach me to do your will, for you are my God; may your good Spirit lead me on level ground.
Psalms 143:10

My TALK with God today

Day

Date

☐	Morning Prayer	☐	Evening Prayer	Choose one or more

ASK

Three Things I am **THANKFUL** for Today:

1.

2.

3.

What do I need forgiveness for?

LET go and let God handle it

Ask God to help with this challenge today.

I set these intentions for the day:

_____

_____

_____

_____

_____

_____

People to keep in my prayers today.

KEEP communicating with God today

A kind deed done today.

_____

_____

_____

_____

_____

Blessings I received today

_____

_____

_____

_____

_____

Get wisdom, get understanding; do not forget my words or turn away from them. Proverbs 4:5

My TALK with God today

Day   **Date**

☐ Morning Prayer	☐ Evening Prayer	Choose one or more

ASK

Three Things I am THANKFUL for Today:

1.

2.

3.

What do I need forgiveness for?

LET go and let God handle it

Ask God to help with this challenge today.

I set these intentions for the day:

_____

_____

_____

_____

_____

_____

People to keep in my prayers today.

KEEP communicating with God today

A kind deed done today.

_____

_____

_____

_____

_____

Blessings I received today

_____

_____

_____

_____

_____

Do not add to what I command you and do not subtract from it, but keep the commands of the Lord your God that I give you.
Deuteronomy 4:2

My TALK with God today → **Day**   **Date**

☐ Morning Prayer	☐ Evening Prayer	Choose one or more

ASK

Three Things I am **THANKFUL** for Today:

1.

2.

3.

What do I need forgiveness for?

LET go and let God handle it

Ask God to help with this challenge today.

I set these intentions for the day:

_____

_____

_____

_____

_____

_____

People to keep in my prayers today.

KEEP communicating with God today

A kind deed done today.

_____

_____

_____

_____

_____

Blessings I received today

_____

_____

_____

_____

_____

Neither do people light a lamp and put it under a bowl. Instead they put it on its stand, and it gives light to everyone in the house. In the same way, let your light shine before others, that they may see your good deeds and glorify your Father in heaven. Matthew 5:15-16

My TALK with God today → **Day**   **Date**

❏ Morning Prayer	❏ Evening Prayer	Choose one or more

ASK

Three Things I am **THANKFUL** for Today:

What do I need forgiveness for?

1.

2.

3.

LET go and let God handle it

Ask God to help with this challenge today.

I set these intentions for the day:

_____

_____

_____

_____

_____

_____

People to keep in my prayers today.

KEEP communicating with God today

A kind deed done today.

Blessings I received today

_____   _____

_____   _____

_____   _____

_____   _____

_____   _____

Wait for the Lord; be strong and take heart and wait for the Lord. Psalms 27:14

My TALK with God today

Day

Date

☐ Morning Prayer	☐ Evening Prayer	Choose one or more

ASK

Three Things I am **THANKFUL** for Today:
1.
2.
3.

What do I need forgiveness for?

LET go and let God handle it

Ask God to help with this challenge today.

I set these intentions for the day:

_____

_____

_____

_____

_____

_____

People to keep in my prayers today.

KEEP communicating with God today

A kind deed done today.

_____

_____

_____

_____

_____

Blessings I received today

_____

_____

_____

_____

_____

May the God who gives endurance and encouragement give you the same attitude of mind toward each other that Christ Jesus had.
Romans 15:5

My TALK with God today

Day

Date

☐ **Morning Prayer** ☐ **Evening Prayer** Choose one or more

ASK

Three Things I am **THANKFUL** for Today:

1.

2.

3.

What do I need forgiveness for?

LET go and let God handle it

Ask God to help with this challenge today.

I set these intentions for the day:

_____

_____

_____

_____

_____

_____

People to keep in my prayers today.

KEEP communicating with God today

A kind deed done today.

_____

_____

_____

_____

Blessings I received today

_____

_____

_____

_____

The Lord longs to be gracious to you; therefore he will rise up to show you compassion. For the Lord is a God of justice. Blessed are all who wait for him! Isaiah 30:18

My TALK with God today

Day

Date

☐ Morning Prayer	☐ Evening Prayer	Choose one or more

ASK

Three Things I am **THANKFUL** for Today:

1.

2.

3.

What do I need forgiveness for?

LET go and let God handle it

Ask God to help with this challenge today.

I set these intentions for the day:

_____

_____

_____

_____

_____

_____

People to keep in my prayers today.

KEEP communicating with God today

A kind deed done today.

_____

_____

_____

_____

_____

Blessings I received today

_____

_____

_____

_____

_____

This is to my Father's glory, that you bear much fruit, showing yourselves to be my disciples.
John 15:8

My TALK with God today → Day   Date

☐ Morning Prayer	☐ Evening Prayer	Choose one or more

Three Things I am **THANKFUL** for Today:
1.
2.
3.

LET go and let God handle it

I set these intentions for the day:

_____

_____

_____

_____

_____

KEEP communicating with God today

A kind deed done today.

_____

_____

_____

_____

_____

Blessings I received today

_____

_____

_____

_____

_____

ASK

What do I need forgiveness for?

Ask God to help with this challenge today.

People to keep in my prayers today.

They devoted themselves to the apostles' teaching and to fellowship, to the breaking of bread and to prayer.
Acts 2:42

My TALK with God today

Day

Date

☐ Morning Prayer	☐ Evening Prayer	Choose one or more

ASK

What do I need forgiveness for?

Three Things I am **THANKFUL** for Today:

1.

2.

3.

LET go and let God handle it

Ask God to help with this challenge today.

I set these intentions for the day:

_____

_____

_____

_____

_____

People to keep in my prayers today.

KEEP communicating with God today

A kind deed done today.

Blessings I received today

_____   _____

_____   _____

_____   _____

_____   _____

_____   _____

Let love and faithfulness never leave you; bind them around your neck, write them on the tablet of your heart. Then you will win favor and a good name in the sight of God and man.
Proverbs 3:3-4

My TALK with God today	Day	Date

☐ Morning Prayer	☐ Evening Prayer	Choose one or more

ASK

Three Things I am THANKFUL for Today:

1.

2.

3.

What do I need forgiveness for?

LET go and let God handle it

Ask God to help with this challenge today.

I set these intentions for the day:

_____

_____

_____

_____

_____

People to keep in my prayers today.

KEEP communicating with God today

A kind deed done today.

_____

_____

_____

_____

Blessings I received today

_____

_____

_____

_____

The eyes of the Lord are on the righteous, and his ears are attentive to their cry.
Psalms 34:15

My TALK with God today   **Day**   **Date**

☐ Morning Prayer	☐ Evening Prayer	Choose one or more	**ASK**

Three Things I am **THANKFUL** for Today:
1.
2.
3.

What do I need forgiveness for?

LET go and let God handle it

Ask God to help with this challenge today.

I set these intentions for the day:

_____

_____

_____

_____

_____

People to keep in my prayers today.

KEEP communicating with God today

A kind deed done today.   **Blessings I received today**

_____   _____

_____   _____

_____   _____

_____   _____

_____   _____

If we hope for what we do not yet have, we wait for it patiently.
Romans 8:25

My TALK with God today → **Day** _____ **Date** _____

☐ Morning Prayer	☐ Evening Prayer	Choose one or more

ASK

What do I need forgiveness for?

Three Things I am **THANKFUL** for Today:
1.
2.
3.

LET go and let God handle it

Ask God to help with this challenge today.

I set these intentions for the day:

_____
_____
_____
_____
_____
_____

People to keep in my prayers today.

KEEP communicating with God today

A kind deed done today.

_____
_____
_____
_____
_____

Blessings I received today

_____
_____
_____
_____
_____

But for that very reason I was shown mercy so that in me, the worst of sinners, Christ Jesus might display his immense patience as an example for those who would believe in him and receive eternal life.
1 Timothy 1:16

My TALK with God today ➤ Day _____ Date _____

☐ Morning Prayer	☐ Evening Prayer	Choose one or more

ASK

What do I need forgiveness for?

Three Things I am **THANKFUL** for Today:

1.

2.

3.

LET go and let God handle it

Ask God to help with this challenge today.

I set these intentions for the day:

_____

_____

_____

_____

_____

_____

People to keep in my prayers today.

KEEP communicating with God today

A kind deed done today.

_____

_____

_____

_____

_____

Blessings I received today

_____

_____

_____

_____

_____

Pay attention to what I say; turn your ear to my words. Do not let them out of your sight, keep them within your heart.
Proverbs 4:20-21

My TALK with God today

Day	Date

☐ Morning Prayer	☐ Evening Prayer	Choose one or more

ASK

Three Things I am THANKFUL for Today:

1.

2.

3.

What do I need forgiveness for?

LET go and let God handle it

Ask God to help with this challenge today.

I set these intentions for the day:

_____

_____

_____

_____

_____

_____

People to keep in my prayers today.

KEEP communicating with God today

A kind deed done today.

_____

_____

_____

_____

_____

Blessings I received today

_____

_____

_____

_____

_____

For the eyes of the Lord are on the righteous and his ears are attentive to their prayer, but the face of the Lord is against those who do evil.
1 Peter 3:12

My TALK with God today

Day

Date

- ☐ Morning Prayer
- ☐ Evening Prayer

Choose one or more

ASK

Three Things I am THANKFUL for Today:

1.

2.

3.

What do I need forgiveness for?

LET go and let God handle it

Ask God to help with this challenge today.

I set these intentions for the day:

_____

_____

_____

_____

_____

_____

People to keep in my prayers today.

KEEP communicating with God today

A kind deed done today.

_____

_____

_____

_____

_____

Blessings I received today

_____

_____

_____

_____

_____

The Lord gives sight to the blind, the Lord lifts up those who are bowed down, the Lord loves the righteous.
Psalms 146:8

My TALK with God today → **Day** **Date**

☐ **Morning Prayer** ☐ **Evening Prayer** Choose one or more | **ASK**

Three Things I am **THANKFUL** for Today:
1.
2.
3.

What do I need forgiveness for?

LET go and let God handle it

Ask God to help with this challenge today.

I set these intentions for the day:

_____
_____
_____
_____
_____
_____

People to keep in my prayers today.

KEEP communicating with God today

A kind deed done today.   **Blessings I received today**

_____ _____
_____ _____
_____ _____
_____ _____
_____ _____

Live in harmony with one another. Do not be proud, but be willing to associate with people of low position. Do not be conceited.
Romans 12:16

My TALK with God today

Day

Date

☐ Morning Prayer	☐ Evening Prayer	Choose one or more

ASK

Three Things I am **THANKFUL** for Today:

1.

2.

3.

LET go and let God handle it

What do I need forgiveness for?

Ask God to help with this challenge today.

I set these intentions for the day:

_____

_____

_____

_____

_____

_____

People to keep in my prayers today.

KEEP communicating with God today

A kind deed done today.

_____

_____

_____

_____

_____

Blessings I received today

_____

_____

_____

_____

_____

Better a patient person than a warrior, one with self-control than one who takes a city.
Proverbs 16:32

My TALK with God today | **Day** | **Date**

☐ Morning Prayer	☐ Evening Prayer	Choose one or more

ASK

Three Things I am **THANKFUL** for Today:

1.

2.

3.

What do I need forgiveness for?

LET go and let God handle it

Ask God to help with this challenge today.

I set these intentions for the day:

_____

_____

_____

_____

_____

People to keep in my prayers today.

KEEP communicating with God today

A kind deed done today.	Blessings I received today
_____	_____
_____	_____
_____	_____
_____	_____
_____	_____

Be still before the Lord and wait patiently for him; do not fret when people succeed in their ways, when they carry out their wicked schemes.
Psalms 37:7

My TALK with God today	Day		Date

☐ Morning Prayer	☐ Evening Prayer	Choose one or more	ASK

Three Things I am **THANKFUL** for Today:
1.
2.
3.

What do I need forgiveness for?

LET go and let God handle it

Ask God to help with this challenge today.

I set these intentions for the day:
_____
_____
_____
_____
_____
_____

People to keep in my prayers today.

KEEP communicating with God today

A kind deed done today.
_____
_____
_____
_____
_____

Blessings I received today
_____
_____
_____
_____
_____

A cheerful heart is good medicine, but a crushed spirit dries up the bones.
Proverbs 17:22

My TALK with God today → **Day**   **Date**

☐ Morning Prayer	☐ Evening Prayer	Choose one or more

ASK

Three Things I am **THANKFUL** for Today:

1.

2.

3.

What do I need forgiveness for?

LET go and let God handle it

Ask God to help with this challenge today.

I set these intentions for the day:

_____

_____

_____

_____

_____

_____

People to keep in my prayers today.

KEEP communicating with God today

A kind deed done today.

_____

_____

_____

_____

_____

Blessings I received today

_____

_____

_____

_____

_____

Accept the one whose faith is weak, without quarreling over disputable matters. Romans 14:1

My TALK with God today → **Day**　　　　　　**Date**

☐ Morning Prayer	☐ Evening Prayer	Choose one or more	**ASK**

Three Things I am **THANKFUL** for Today:
1.
2.
3.

What do I need
forgiveness for?

LET go and let God handle it

Ask God to help with this
challenge today.

I set these intentions for the day:
_____
_____
_____
_____
_____
_____

People to keep in my
prayers today.

KEEP communicating with God today

A kind deed done today.　　　Blessings I received today
_____　　　_____
_____　　　_____
_____　　　_____
_____　　　_____
_____　　　_____

They all joined
together constantly in
prayer, along with the
women and Mary the
mother of Jesus, and
with his brothers.
Acts 1:14

My TALK with God today

Day

Date

☐ Morning Prayer ☐ Evening Prayer Choose one or more

ASK

What do I need forgiveness for?

Three Things I am **THANKFUL** for Today:

1.

2.

3.

LET go and let God handle it

Ask God to help with this challenge today.

I set these intentions for the day:

_____

_____

_____

_____

_____

_____

People to keep in my prayers today.

KEEP communicating with God today

A kind deed done today.

Blessings I received today

_____

_____

_____

_____

_____

Unless the Lord builds the house, the builders labor in vain. Unless the Lord watches over the city, the guards stand watch in vain.
Psalms 127:1

My TALK with God today

Day _____ **Date** _____

☐ Morning Prayer	☐ Evening Prayer	Choose one or more

ASK

What do I need forgiveness for?

Three Things I am **THANKFUL** for Today:

1.

2.

3.

LET go and let God handle it

Ask God to help with this challenge today.

I set these intentions for the day:

_____

_____

_____

_____

_____

_____

People to keep in my prayers today.

KEEP communicating with God today

A kind deed done today.

_____

_____

_____

_____

_____

Blessings I received today

_____

_____

_____

_____

_____

He who finds a wife finds what is good and receives favor from the Lord.
Proverbs 18:22

My TALK with God today **Day** **Date**

☐ Morning Prayer	☐ Evening Prayer	Choose one or more

Three Things I am **THANKFUL** for Today:

1.

2.

3.

LET go and let God handle it

I set these intentions for the day:

_____

_____

_____

_____

_____

_____

KEEP communicating with God today

A kind deed done today.

_____

_____

_____

_____

_____

Blessings I received today

_____

_____

_____

_____

_____

ASK

What do I need forgiveness for?

Ask God to help with this challenge today.

People to keep in my prayers today.

Those who are in the realm of the flesh cannot please God.
Romans 8:8

My TALK with God today | **Day** | **Date**

☐ Morning Prayer	☐ Evening Prayer	Choose one or more

ASK

Three Things I am **THANKFUL** for Today:

1.

2.

3.

What do I need forgiveness for?

LET go and let God handle it

Ask God to help with this challenge today.

I set these intentions for the day:

_____

_____

_____

_____

_____

_____

People to keep in my prayers today.

KEEP communicating with God today

A kind deed done today.

_____

_____

_____

_____

_____

Blessings I received today

_____

_____

_____

_____

_____

But do not forget this one thing, dear friends: With the Lord a day is like a thousand years, and a thousand years are like a day.
2 Peter 3:8

My TALK with God today | **Day** | **Date**

| ☐ Morning Prayer | ☐ Evening Prayer | Choose one or more |

ASK

Three Things I am **THANKFUL** for Today:

1.

2.

3.

What do I need forgiveness for?

LET go and let God handle it

Ask God to help with this challenge today.

I set these intentions for the day:

_____

_____

_____

_____

_____

_____

People to keep in my prayers today.

KEEP communicating with God today

A kind deed done today.

_____

_____

_____

_____

_____

Blessings I received today

_____

_____

_____

_____

_____

Therefore keep watch, because you do not know on what day your Lord will come. Matthew 24:42

My TALK with God today

Day　　　　　　　**Date**

| ☐ | Morning Prayer | ☐ | Evening Prayer | Choose one or more |

ASK

Three Things I am **THANKFUL** for Today:

1.

2.

3.

What do I need forgiveness for?

LET go and let God handle it

Ask God to help with this challenge today.

I set these intentions for the day:

_____

_____

_____

_____

_____

_____

People to keep in my prayers today.

KEEP communicating with God today

A kind deed done today.　　Blessings I received today

_____　　_____

_____　　_____

_____　　_____

_____　　_____

_____

Restore us, Lord God Almighty; make your face shine on us, that we may be saved.
Psalms 80:19

My TALK with God today

Day

Date

☐ Morning Prayer	☐ Evening Prayer	Choose one or more

ASK

Three Things I am **THANKFUL** for Today:

1.

2.

3.

What do I need forgiveness for?

LET go and let God handle it

Ask God to help with this challenge today.

I set these intentions for the day:

_____

_____

_____

_____

_____

_____

People to keep in my prayers today.

KEEP communicating with God today

A kind deed done today.

_____

_____

_____

_____

Blessings I received today

_____

_____

_____

_____

When times are good, be happy; but when times are bad, consider this: God has made the one as well as the other. Therefore, no one can discover anything about their future. Ecclesiastes 7:14

My TALK with God today

Day ➤   Date

☐ Morning Prayer	☐ Evening Prayer	Choose one or more

ASK

Three Things I am THANKFUL for Today:

1.

2.

3.

What do I need forgiveness for?

LET go and let God handle it

Ask God to help with this challenge today.

I set these intentions for the day:

_____

_____

_____

_____

_____

People to keep in my prayers today.

KEEP communicating with God today

A kind deed done today.

_____

_____

_____

_____

_____

Blessings I received today

_____

_____

_____

_____

_____

A generous person will prosper; whoever refreshes others will be refreshed.
Proverbs 11:25

My TALK with God today → **Day**   **Date**

☐ Morning Prayer	☐ Evening Prayer	Choose one or more

ASK

Three Things I am **THANKFUL** for Today:

1.

2.

3.

What do I need forgiveness for?

LET go and let God handle it

Ask God to help with this challenge today.

I set these intentions for the day:

_____

_____

_____

_____

_____

_____

People to keep in my prayers today.

KEEP communicating with God today

A kind deed done today.

_____

_____

_____

_____

_____

Blessings I received today

_____

_____

_____

_____

_____

Praise be to the Lord, to God our Savior, who daily bears our burdens.
Psalms 68:19

My TALK with God today → **Day** **Date**

☐ Morning Prayer	☐ Evening Prayer	Choose one or more

ASK

Three Things I am **THANKFUL** for Today:

1.

2.

3.

What do I need forgiveness for?

LET go and let God handle it

Ask God to help with this challenge today.

I set these intentions for the day:

_____

_____

_____

_____

_____

_____

People to keep in my prayers today.

KEEP communicating with God today

A kind deed done today.

_____

_____

_____

_____

_____

Blessings I received today

_____

_____

_____

_____

_____

The Lord sends poverty and wealth; he humbles and he exalts.
1 Samuel 2:7

My TALK with God today

Day

Date

☐	Morning Prayer	☐	Evening Prayer	Choose one or more

ASK

Three Things I am **THANKFUL** for Today:

1.

2.

3.

What do I need forgiveness for?

LET go and let God handle it

Ask God to help with this challenge today.

I set these intentions for the day:

_____

_____

_____

_____

_____

_____

People to keep in my prayers today.

KEEP communicating with God today

A kind deed done today.

_____

_____

_____

_____

_____

Blessings I received today

_____

_____

_____

_____

_____

Rejoice with those who rejoice; mourn with those who mourn.
Romans 12:15

My TALK with God today → **Day** | **Date**

☐ **Morning Prayer** ☐ **Evening Prayer** | Choose one or more | **ASK**

Three Things I am **THANKFUL** for Today:

1.

2.

3.

LET go and let God handle it

What do I need forgiveness for?

Ask God to help with this challenge today.

I set these intentions for the day:

_____
_____
_____
_____
_____
_____

People to keep in my prayers today.

KEEP communicating with God today

A kind deed done today.
_____
_____
_____
_____
_____

Blessings I received today
_____
_____
_____
_____
_____

When you pass through the waters, I will be with you; and when you pass through the rivers, they will not sweep over you. When you walk through the fire, you will not be burned; the flames will not set you ablaze.
Isaiah 43:2

My TALK with God today

Day	Date

☐ Morning Prayer	☐ Evening Prayer	Choose one or more	**ASK**

Three Things I am **THANKFUL** for Today:

1.

2.

3.

What do I need forgiveness for?

LET go and let God handle it

Ask God to help with this challenge today.

I set these intentions for the day:

_____

_____

_____

_____

_____

_____

_____

People to keep in my prayers today.

KEEP communicating with God today

A kind deed done today.

Blessings I received today

_____ _____

_____ _____

_____ _____

_____ _____

_____ _____

Let us consider how we may spur one another on toward love and good deeds, not giving up meeting together, as some are in the habit of doing, but encouraging one another—and all the more as you see the Day approaching.
Hebrews 10:24-25

My TALK with God today	Day	Date

☐ Morning Prayer	☐ Evening Prayer	Choose one or more	ASK

Three Things I am **THANKFUL** for Today:
1.
2.
3.

What do I need forgiveness for?

LET go and let God handle it

Ask God to help with this challenge today.

I set these intentions for the day:

_____

_____

_____

_____

_____

People to keep in my prayers today.

KEEP communicating with God today

A kind deed done today.	Blessings I received today
_____	_____
_____	_____
_____	_____
_____	_____

All the believers were one in heart and mind. No one claimed that any of their possessions was their own, but they shared everything they had. Acts 4:32

My TALK with God today

Day

Date

☐ Morning Prayer ☐ Evening Prayer Choose one or more

ASK

Three Things I am **THANKFUL** for Today:

1.

2.

3.

LET go and let God handle it

What do I need forgiveness for?

Ask God to help with this challenge today.

I set these intentions for the day:

_____

_____

_____

_____

_____

_____

People to keep in my prayers today.

KEEP communicating with God today

A kind deed done today.   **Blessings I received today**

_____ _____

_____ _____

_____ _____

_____ _____

_____ _____

Be strong and take heart, all you who hope in the Lord. Psalms 31:24

My TALK with God today

Day

Date

☐ Morning Prayer	☐ Evening Prayer	Choose one or more

Three Things I am **THANKFUL** for Today:

1.

2.

3.

LET go and let God handle it

I set these intentions for the day:

_____

_____

_____

_____

_____

_____

ASK

What do I need forgiveness for?

Ask God to help with this challenge today.

People to keep in my prayers today.

KEEP communicating with God today

A kind deed done today.

_____

_____

_____

_____

_____

Blessings I received today

_____

_____

_____

_____

_____

Be on your guard;
stand firm in the faith;
be courageous;
be strong.
1 Corinthians 16:13

My TALK with God today

Day ____ **Date** ____

☐ Morning Prayer	☐ Evening Prayer	Choose one or more

Three Things I am **THANKFUL** for Today:

1.

2.

3.

LET go and let God handle it

I set these intentions for the day:

_____

_____

_____

_____

_____

_____

ASK

What do I need forgiveness for?

Ask God to help with this challenge today.

People to keep in my prayers today.

KEEP communicating with God today

A kind deed done today.	Blessings I received today
_____	_____
_____	_____
_____	_____
_____	_____
_____	_____

For if the willingness is there, the gift is acceptable according to what one has, not according to what one does not have.
2 Corinthians 8:12

My TALK with God today → **Day**   **Date**

☐ Morning Prayer	☐ Evening Prayer	Choose one or more

ASK

Three Things I am **THANKFUL** for Today:
1.
2.
3.

What do I need forgiveness for?

LET go and let God handle it

Ask God to help with this challenge today.

I set these intentions for the day:

_____
_____
_____
_____
_____
_____

People to keep in my prayers today.

KEEP communicating with God today

A kind deed done today.

_____
_____
_____
_____
_____

Blessings I received today

_____
_____
_____
_____
_____

Humble yourselves before the Lord, and he will lift you up. James 4:10

My TALK with God today → **Day**   **Date**

☐ Morning Prayer	☐ Evening Prayer	Choose one or more

ASK

Three Things I am **THANKFUL** for Today:

1.

2.

3.

What do I need forgiveness for?

LET go and let God handle it

Ask God to help with this challenge today.

I set these intentions for the day:

_____

_____

_____

_____

_____

_____

People to keep in my prayers today.

KEEP communicating with God today

A kind deed done today.   Blessings I received today

_____   _____

_____   _____

_____   _____

_____   _____

_____   _____

Pride brings a person low, but the lowly in spirit gain honor.
Proverbs 29:23

My TALK with God today **Day** **Date**

☐ Morning Prayer	☐ Evening Prayer	Choose one or more

ASK

Three Things I am THANKFUL for Today:

1.

2.

3.

What do I need forgiveness for?

LET go and let God handle it

Ask God to help with this challenge today.

I set these intentions for the day:

_____

_____

_____

_____

_____

_____

People to keep in my prayers today.

KEEP communicating with God today

A kind deed done today.

_____

_____

_____

_____

_____

Blessings I received today

_____

_____

_____

_____

_____

Finally, all of you, be like-minded, be sympathetic, love one another, be compassionate and humble.
1 Peter 3:8

My TALK with God today

Day		Date

☐ Morning Prayer	☐ Evening Prayer	Choose one or more

ASK

Three Things I am **THANKFUL** for Today:

1.

2.

3.

What do I need forgiveness for?

LET go and let God handle it

Ask God to help with this challenge today.

I set these intentions for the day:

_____

_____

_____

_____

_____

_____

People to keep in my prayers today.

KEEP communicating with God today

A kind deed done today.   Blessings I received today

_____   _____

_____   _____

_____   _____

_____   _____

_____   _____

God chose the lowly things of this world and the despised things—and the things that are not— to nullify the things that are, so that no one may boast before him.
1 Corinthians 1:28-29

My TALK with God today

Day

Date

☐ Morning Prayer	☐ Evening Prayer	Choose one or more

ASK

Three Things I am **THANKFUL** for Today:

1.

2.

3.

What do I need forgiveness for?

LET go and let God handle it

Ask God to help with this challenge today.

I set these intentions for the day:

_____

_____

_____

_____

_____

_____

People to keep in my prayers today.

KEEP communicating with God today

A kind deed done today.

_____

_____

_____

_____

_____

Blessings I received today

_____

_____

_____

_____

_____

For the Lord takes delight in his people; he crowns the humble with victory.
Psalms 149:4

My TALK with God today | **Day** | **Date**

☐ Morning Prayer	☐ Evening Prayer	Choose one or more

Three Things I am **THANKFUL** for Today:

1.

2.

3.

What do I need forgiveness for?

LET go and let God handle it

Ask God to help with this challenge today.

I set these intentions for the day:
_____
_____
_____
_____
_____
_____

People to keep in my prayers today.

KEEP communicating with God today

A kind deed done today.
_____
_____
_____
_____
_____

Blessings I received today
_____
_____
_____
_____
_____

For even the Son of Man did not come to be served, but to serve, and to give his life as a ransom for many. Mark 10:45

My TALK with God today	**Day**	**Date**

☐ Morning Prayer	☐ Evening Prayer	Choose one or more	**ASK**

Three Things I am **THANKFUL** for Today:

1.

2.

3.

LET go and let God handle it

I set these intentions for the day:

_____

_____

_____

_____

_____

_____

KEEP communicating with God today

A kind deed done today.

_____

_____

_____

_____

_____

Blessings I received today

_____

_____

_____

_____

_____

What do I need forgiveness for?

Ask God to help with this challenge today.

People to keep in my prayers today.

Come, let us bow down in worship, let us kneel before the Lord our Maker. Psalms 95:6

My TALK with God today	Day	Date

☐ Morning Prayer	☐ Evening Prayer	Choose one or more

ASK

Three Things I am **THANKFUL** for Today:

1.

2.

3.

What do I need forgiveness for?

LET go and let God handle it

Ask God to help with this challenge today.

I set these intentions for the day:

_____

_____

_____

_____

_____

People to keep in my prayers today.

KEEP communicating with God today

A kind deed done today.

_____

_____

_____

_____

_____

Blessings I received today

_____

_____

_____

_____

_____

I can do everything through him who gives me strength.
Philippians 4:13

My TALK with God today → **Day**   **Date**

☐ Morning Prayer	☐ Evening Prayer	Choose one or more	**ASK**

Three Things I am THANKFUL for Today:

1.

2.

3.

LET go and let God handle it

What do I need forgiveness for?

I set these intentions for the day:

_____

_____

_____

_____

_____

_____

Ask God to help with this challenge today.

People to keep in my prayers today.

KEEP communicating with God today

A kind deed done today.

_____

_____

_____

_____

_____

Blessings I received today

_____

_____

_____

_____

_____

All Scripture is God-breathed and is useful for teaching, rebuking, correcting and training in righteousness
2 Timothy 3:16

My TALK with God today → **Day**   **Date**

☐ Morning Prayer	☐ Evening Prayer	Choose one or more

ASK

Three Things I am **THANKFUL** for Today:

1.

2.

3.

What do I need forgiveness for?

LET go and let God handle it

Ask God to help with this challenge today.

I set these intentions for the day:

_____

_____

_____

_____

_____

_____

People to keep in my prayers today.

KEEP communicating with God today

A kind deed done today.

_____

_____

_____

_____

Blessings I received today

_____

_____

_____

_____

By day the Lord directs his love, at night his song is with me— a prayer to the God of my life.
Psalms 42:8

My TALK with God today → **Day** **Date**

☐ Morning Prayer	☐ Evening Prayer	Choose one or more

ASK

Three Things I am **THANKFUL** for Today:

1.

2.

3.

LET go and let God handle it

What do I need forgiveness for?

Ask God to help with this challenge today.

I set these intentions for the day:

_____

_____

_____

_____

_____

_____

People to keep in my prayers today.

KEEP communicating with God today

A kind deed done today.

_____

_____

_____

_____

_____

Blessings I received today

_____

_____

_____

_____

_____

Whoever loves discipline loves knowledge, but whoever hates correction is stupid.
Proverbs 12:1

My TALK with God today | **Day** | **Date**

| ☐ Morning Prayer | ☐ Evening Prayer | Choose one or more |

ASK

Three Things I am THANKFUL for Today:

1.

2.

3.

What do I need forgiveness for?

LET go and let God handle it

Ask God to help with this challenge today.

I set these intentions for the day:

_____

_____

_____

_____

_____

_____

People to keep in my prayers today.

KEEP communicating with God today

A kind deed done today.

_____

_____

_____

_____

_____

Blessings I received today

_____

_____

_____

_____

_____

We fasted and petitioned our God about this, and he answered our prayer.
Ezra 8:23

My TALK with God today

Day _____ **Date** _____

☐ Morning Prayer	☐ Evening Prayer	Choose one or more

Three Things I am **THANKFUL** for Today:

1.

2.

3.

LET go and let God handle it

I set these intentions for the day:

_____

_____

_____

_____

_____

_____

KEEP communicating with God today

A kind deed done today.

_____

_____

_____

_____

_____

Blessings I received today

_____

_____

_____

_____

_____

ASK

What do I need forgiveness for?

Ask God to help with this challenge today.

People to keep in my prayers today.

We know that in all things God works for the good of those who love him, who have been called according to his purpose.
Romans 8:28

My TALK with God today → **Day** **Date**

☐ Morning Prayer	☐ Evening Prayer	Choose one or more

ASK

Three Things I am THANKFUL for Today:

1.

2.

3.

What do I need forgiveness for?

LET go and let God handle it

Ask God to help with this challenge today.

I set these intentions for the day:

_____

_____

_____

_____

_____

_____

People to keep in my prayers today.

KEEP communicating with God today

A kind deed done today.

_____

_____

_____

_____

_____

Blessings I received today

_____

_____

_____

_____

_____

The Lord is faithful, and he will strengthen you and protect you from the evil one.
2 Thessalonians 3:3

My TALK with God today	Day	Date

☐ Morning Prayer	☐ Evening Prayer	Choose one or more	ASK

Three Things I am **THANKFUL** for Today:

1.

2.

3.

What do I need forgiveness for?

LET go and let God handle it

Ask God to help with this challenge today.

I set these intentions for the day:

_____

_____

_____

_____

_____

_____

People to keep in my prayers today.

KEEP communicating with God today

A kind deed done today.	Blessings I received today
_____	_____
_____	_____
_____	_____
_____	_____
_____	_____

Lord, you are my God; I will exalt you and praise your name, for in perfect faithfulness you have done wonderful things, things planned long ago.
Isaiah 25:1

My TALK with God today

Day		Date

☐ Morning Prayer	☐ Evening Prayer	Choose one or more

ASK

Three Things I am **THANKFUL** for Today:
1.
2.
3.

What do I need forgiveness for?

LET go and let God handle it

Ask God to help with this challenge today.

I set these intentions for the day:

_____

_____

_____

_____

_____

_____

People to keep in my prayers today.

KEEP communicating with God today

A kind deed done today.	Blessings I received today
_____	_____
_____	_____
_____	_____
_____	_____
_____	_____

Wisdom's instruction is to fear the Lord, and humility comes before honor.
Proverbs 15:33

My TALK with God today	Day	Date

☐ Morning Prayer	☐ Evening Prayer	Choose one or more	ASK

Three Things I am **THANKFUL** for Today:

1.

2.

3.

LET go and let God handle it

I set these intentions for the day:

_____

_____

_____

_____

_____

_____

ASK

What do I need forgiveness for?

Ask God to help with this challenge today.

People to keep in my prayers today.

KEEP communicating with God today

A kind deed done today.

_____

_____

_____

_____

_____

Blessings I received today

_____

_____

_____

_____

_____

Know therefore that the Lord your God is God; he is the faithful God, keeping his covenant of love to a thousand generations of those who love him and keep his commandments. Deuteronomy 7:9

My TALK with God today ➤ **Day** _____ **Date** _____

☐ Morning Prayer	☐ Evening Prayer	Choose one or more

Three Things I am **THANKFUL** for Today:
1.
2.
3.

LET go and let God handle it

I set these intentions for the day:

_____

_____

_____

_____

_____

_____

ASK

What do I need forgiveness for?

Ask God to help with this challenge today.

People to keep in my prayers today.

KEEP communicating with God today

A kind deed done today.	Blessings I received today
_____	_____
_____	_____
_____	_____
_____	_____
_____	_____

No temptation has overtaken you except what is common to mankind. And God is faithful; he will not let you be tempted beyond what you can bear. But when you are tempted, he will also provide a way out so that you can endure it.
1 Corinthians 10:13

My TALK with God today → **Day**

Date

☐ Morning Prayer	☐ Evening Prayer	Choose one or more

ASK

Three Things I am **THANKFUL** for Today:

1.

2.

3.

What do I need forgiveness for?

LET go and let God handle it

Ask God to help with this challenge today.

I set these intentions for the day:

_____
_____
_____
_____
_____
_____

People to keep in my prayers today.

KEEP communicating with God today

A kind deed done today.   **Blessings I received today**

_____   _____
_____   _____
_____   _____
_____   _____
_____   _____

Until now you have not asked for anything in my name. Ask and you will receive, and your joy will be complete.
John 16:24

My TALK with God today ➤ **Day**   **Date**

☐ Morning Prayer	☐ Evening Prayer	Choose one or more

ASK

Three Things I am **THANKFUL** for Today:
1.
2.
3.

What do I need forgiveness for?

LET go and let God handle it

Ask God to help with this challenge today.

I set these intentions for the day:

_____

_____

_____

_____

_____

_____

People to keep in my prayers today.

KEEP communicating with God today

A kind deed done today.

_____

_____

_____

_____

_____

Blessings I received today

_____

_____

_____

_____

_____

You, Lord, are forgiving and good, abounding in love to all
who call to you.
Psalms 86:5

My TALK with God today	Day		Date

☐ Morning Prayer	☐ Evening Prayer	Choose one or more	ASK

Three Things I am **THANKFUL** for Today:

1.

2.

3.

What do I need forgiveness for?

LET go and let God handle it

Ask God to help with this challenge today.

I set these intentions for the day:

_____

_____

_____

_____

_____

_____

People to keep in my prayers today.

KEEP communicating with God today

A kind deed done today.

_____

_____

_____

_____

_____

Blessings I received today

_____

_____

_____

_____

_____

You, Lord, reign forever; your throne endures from generation to generation.
Lamentations 5:19

My TALK with God today | **Day** | **Date**

| ☐ Morning Prayer | ☐ Evening Prayer | Choose one or more |

ASK

What do I need forgiveness for?

Three Things I am **THANKFUL** for Today:

1.

2.

3.

LET go and let God handle it

Ask God to help with this challenge today.

I set these intentions for the day:

_____

_____

_____

_____

_____

_____

People to keep in my prayers today.

KEEP communicating with God today

A kind deed done today.

_____

_____

_____

_____

Blessings I received today

_____

_____

_____

_____

For I know that through your prayers and God's provision of the Spirit of Jesus Christ what has happened to me will turn out for my deliverance.
Philippians 1:19

My TALK with God today | **Day** | **Date**

☐ Morning Prayer	☐ Evening Prayer	Choose one or more

ASK

Three Things I am **THANKFUL** for Today:

1.

2.

3.

LET go and let God handle it

I set these intentions for the day:
_____
_____
_____
_____
_____
_____

What do I need forgiveness for?

Ask God to help with this challenge today.

People to keep in my prayers today.

KEEP communicating with God today

A kind deed done today.
_____
_____
_____
_____
_____

Blessings I received today
_____
_____
_____
_____
_____

So that I may come to you with joy, by God's will, and in your company be refreshed.
Romans 15:32

My TALK with God today　　　**Day**　　　**Date**

☐ Morning Prayer	☐ Evening Prayer	Choose one or more

ASK

Three Things I am **THANKFUL** for Today:

1.

2.

3.

What do I need forgiveness for?

LET go and let God handle it

Ask God to help with this challenge today.

I set these intentions for the day:

_____

_____

_____

_____

_____

_____

People to keep in my prayers today.

KEEP communicating with God today

A kind deed done today.

_____

_____

_____

_____

_____

Blessings I received today

_____

_____

_____

_____

_____

The one who calls you
is faithful, and
he will do it.
1 Thessalonians 5:24

My TALK with God today

Day

Date

☐ Morning Prayer	☐ Evening Prayer	Choose one or more

Three Things I am **THANKFUL** for Today:

1.

2.

3.

LET go and let God handle it

ASK

What do I need forgiveness for?

Ask God to help with this challenge today.

I set these intentions for the day:

_____

_____

_____

_____

_____

People to keep in my prayers today.

KEEP communicating with God today

A kind deed done today.

_____

_____

_____

_____

Blessings I received today

_____

_____

_____

_____

For the word of the
Lord is right and true;
he is faithful
in all he does.
Psalms 33:4

My TALK with God today ➤	Day		Date

☐ Morning Prayer	☐ Evening Prayer	Choose one or more	ASK

Three Things I am **THANKFUL** for Today:

1.

2.

3.

What do I need forgiveness for?

LET go and let God handle it

Ask God to help with this challenge today.

I set these intentions for the day:

_____

_____

_____

_____

_____

_____

People to keep in my prayers today.

KEEP communicating with God today

A kind deed done today.	Blessings I received today
_____	_____
_____	_____
_____	_____
_____	_____
_____	_____

God is faithful, who has called you into fellowship with his Son, Jesus Christ our Lord.
1 Corinthians 1:9

My TALK with God today | **Day** | **Date**

| ☐ Morning Prayer | ☐ Evening Prayer | Choose one or more | **ASK** |

What do I need forgiveness for?

| Three Things I am **THANKFUL** for Today: |
| 1. |
| 2. |
| 3. |

LET go and let God handle it

Ask God to help with this challenge today.

I set these intentions for the day:

_____

_____

_____

_____

_____

_____

People to keep in my prayers today.

KEEP communicating with God today

A kind deed done today.

_____

_____

_____

_____

_____

Blessings I received today

_____

_____

_____

_____

_____

Then he touched their eyes and said, "According to your faith let it be done to you"; Matthew 9:29

My TALK with God today → **Day**   **Date**

☐ Morning Prayer	☐ Evening Prayer	Choose one or more

ASK

Three Things I am **THANKFUL** for Today:

1.

2.

3.

What do I need forgiveness for?

LET go and let God handle it

Ask God to help with this challenge today.

I set these intentions for the day:

_____

_____

_____

_____

_____

_____

People to keep in my prayers today.

KEEP communicating with God today

A kind deed done today.

_____

_____

_____

_____

_____

Blessings I received today

_____

_____

_____

_____

_____

The enemy is puffed up; his desires are not upright— but the righteous person will live by his faithfulness. Habakkuk 2:4

My TALK with God today

Day   **Date**

☐ Morning Prayer	☐ Evening Prayer	Choose one or more

ASK

What do I need forgiveness for?

Three Things I am THANKFUL for Today:

1.

2.

3.

LET go and let God handle it

Ask God to help with this challenge today.

I set these intentions for the day:

_____

_____

_____

_____

_____

_____

People to keep in my prayers today.

KEEP communicating with God today

A kind deed done today.

_____

_____

_____

_____

_____

Blessings I received today

_____

_____

_____

_____

_____

Whatever you do, work at it with all your heart, as working for the Lord, not for human masters, since you know that you will receive an inheritance from the Lord as a reward. It is the Lord Christ you are serving.
Colossians 3:23-24

My TALK with God today

Day

Date

☐ Morning Prayer	☐ Evening Prayer	Choose one or more

ASK

Three Things I am **THANKFUL** for Today:

1.

2.

3.

What do I need forgiveness for?

LET go and let God handle it

Ask God to help with this challenge today.

I set these intentions for the day:

_____

_____

_____

_____

_____

_____

People to keep in my prayers today.

KEEP communicating with God today

A kind deed done today.

_____

_____

_____

_____

_____

Blessings I received today

_____

_____

_____

_____

_____

Heal the sick, raise the dead, cleanse those who have leprosy, drive out demons. Freely you have received; freely give.
Matthew 10:8

My TALK with God today　　**Day**　　　　　**Date**

☐ Morning Prayer	☐ Evening Prayer	Choose one or more

ASK

Three Things I am **THANKFUL** for Today:

1.

2.

3.

What do I need forgiveness for?

LET go and let God handle it

Ask God to help with this challenge today.

I set these intentions for the day:

_____

_____

_____

_____

_____

_____

People to keep in my prayers today.

KEEP communicating with God today

A kind deed done today.　　Blessings I received today

_____　　_____

_____　　_____

_____　　_____

_____　　_____

_____　　_____

Through him all things were made; without him nothing was made that has been made.
John 1:3

My TALK with God today | **Day** | **Date**

| ☐ Morning Prayer | ☐ Evening Prayer | Choose one or more |

ASK

Three Things I am **THANKFUL** for Today:

1.

2.

3.

What do I need forgiveness for?

LET go and let God handle it

Ask God to help with this challenge today.

I set these intentions for the day:

_____

_____

_____

_____

_____

_____

People to keep in my prayers today.

KEEP communicating with God today

A kind deed done today.

_____

_____

_____

_____

_____

Blessings I received today

_____

_____

_____

_____

Let everything that has breath praise the Lord. Praise the Lord. Psalms 150:6

My TALK with God today **Day** **Date**

☐ Morning Prayer	☐ Evening Prayer	Choose one or more

ASK

Three Things I am **THANKFUL** for Today:

1.

2.

3.

What do I need forgiveness for?

LET go and let God handle it

Ask God to help with this challenge today.

I set these intentions for the day:

_____

_____

_____

_____

_____

People to keep in my prayers today.

KEEP communicating with God today

A kind deed done today.	Blessings I received today
_____	_____
_____	_____
_____	_____
_____	_____
_____	_____

If any of you lacks wisdom, you should ask God, who gives generously to all without finding fault, and it will be given to you.
James 1:5

My TALK with God today → **Day**   **Date**

☐ **Morning Prayer**	☐ **Evening Prayer**	Choose one or more

ASK

Three Things I am **THANKFUL** for Today:

1.

2.

3.

What do I need forgiveness for?

LET go and let God handle it

Ask God to help with this challenge today.

I set these intentions for the day:

_____

_____

_____

_____

_____

_____

People to keep in my prayers today.

KEEP communicating with God today

A kind deed done today.   **Blessings I received today**

_____   _____

_____   _____

_____   _____

_____   _____

_____   _____

Praise the Lord, my soul; all my inmost being, praise his holy name.
Psalms 103:1

My TALK with God today	Day		Date

☐ Morning Prayer	☐ Evening Prayer	Choose one or more	**ASK**

Three Things I am **THANKFUL** for Today:
1.
2.
3.

What do I need forgiveness for?

LET go and let God handle it

Ask God to help with this challenge today.

I set these intentions for the day:
_____
_____
_____
_____
_____
_____

People to keep in my prayers today.

KEEP communicating with God today

A kind deed done today.	Blessings I received today
_____	_____
_____	_____
_____	_____
_____	_____
_____	_____

Therefore, as God's chosen people, holy and dearly loved, clothe yourselves with compassion, kindness, humility, gentleness and patience.
Colossians 3:12

My TALK with God today → **Day**   **Date**

☐ Morning Prayer	☐ Evening Prayer	Choose one or more

ASK

Three Things I am **THANKFUL** for Today:

1.

2.

3.

LET go and let God handle it

What do I need forgiveness for?

Ask God to help with this challenge today.

I set these intentions for the day:

_____

_____

_____

_____

_____

_____

People to keep in my prayers today.

KEEP communicating with God today

A kind deed done today.

_____

_____

_____

_____

_____

Blessings I received today

_____

_____

_____

_____

_____

The one who gets wisdom loves life; the one who cherishes understanding will soon prosper.
Proverbs 19:8

My TALK with God today | **Day** | **Date**

☐ Morning Prayer	☐ Evening Prayer	Choose one or more

ASK

What do I need forgiveness for?

Three Things I am **THANKFUL** for Today:

1.

2.

3.

LET go and let God handle it

Ask God to help with this challenge today.

I set these intentions for the day:

_____

_____

_____

_____

_____

_____

People to keep in my prayers today.

KEEP communicating with God today

A kind deed done today.

_____

_____

_____

_____

_____

Blessings I received today

_____

_____

_____

_____

_____

The shepherds returned, glorifying and praising God for all the things they had heard and seen, which were just as they had been told.
Luke 2:20

My TALK with God today **Day**   **Date**

☐ Morning Prayer	☐ Evening Prayer	Choose one or more

ASK

Three Things I am **THANKFUL** for Today:
1.
2.
3.

What do I need forgiveness for?

LET go and let God handle it

Ask God to help with this challenge today.

I set these intentions for the day:
_____
_____
_____
_____
_____
_____

People to keep in my prayers today.

KEEP communicating with God today

A kind deed done today.   Blessings I received today
_____   _____
_____   _____
_____   _____
_____   _____
_____   _____

My mouth is filled with your praise, declaring your splendor all day long. Psalms 71:8

My TALK with God today ➤ Day _____ Date _____

☐ Morning Prayer	☐ Evening Prayer	Choose one or more

ASK

Three Things I am **THANKFUL** for Today:

1.

2.

3.

What do I need forgiveness for?

LET go and let God handle it

Ask God to help with this challenge today.

I set these intentions for the day:

_____

_____

_____

_____

_____

_____

People to keep in my prayers today.

KEEP communicating with God today

A kind deed done today.

_____

_____

_____

_____

_____

Blessings I received today

_____

_____

_____

_____

_____

Accept one another, then, just as Christ accepted you, in order to bring praise to God.
Romans 15:7

My TALK with God today	Day	Date

☐ Morning Prayer	☐ Evening Prayer	Choose one or more

ASK

Three Things I am **THANKFUL** for Today:

1.

2.

3.

What do I need forgiveness for?

LET go and let God handle it

Ask God to help with this challenge today.

I set these intentions for the day:

_____

_____

_____

_____

_____

_____

People to keep in my prayers today.

KEEP communicating with God today

A kind deed done today.

Blessings I received today

_____ _____

_____ _____

_____ _____

_____ _____

_____ _____

For the word of God is alive and active. Sharper than any double-edged sword, it penetrates even to dividing soul and spirit, joints and marrow; it judges the thoughts and attitudes of the heart. Hebrews 4:12

My TALK with God today

Day

Date

☐ Morning Prayer	☐ Evening Prayer	Choose one or more

ASK

Three Things I am **THANKFUL** for Today:

1.

2.

3.

What do I need forgiveness for?

LET go and let God handle it

Ask God to help with this challenge today.

I set these intentions for the day:

_____

_____

_____

_____

_____

_____

People to keep in my prayers today.

KEEP communicating with God today

A kind deed done today.

Blessings I received today

_____   _____

_____   _____

_____   _____

_____   _____

_____   _____

Your word is a lamp for my feet, a light on my path.
Psalms 119:105

My TALK with God today

Day

Date

☐	Morning Prayer	☐	Evening Prayer	Choose one or more

ASK

Three Things I am **THANKFUL** for Today:

What do I need forgiveness for?

1.

2.

3.

LET go and let God handle it

Ask God to help with this challenge today.

I set these intentions for the day:
_____
_____
_____
_____
_____
_____

People to keep in my prayers today.

KEEP communicating with God today

A kind deed done today.

Blessings I received today

_____   _____

_____   _____

_____   _____

_____   _____

_____   _____

Do everything without grumbling or arguing, so that you may become blameless and pure, children of God without fault in a warped and crooked generation. Then you will shine among them like stars in the sky as you hold firmly to the word of life.
Philippians 2:14-16

My TALK with God today

Day

Date

☐ Morning Prayer	☐ Evening Prayer	Choose one or more

ASK

Three Things I am **THANKFUL** for Today:

1.

2.

3.

LET go and let God handle it

What do I need forgiveness for?

Ask God to help with this challenge today.

I set these intentions for the day:

_____

_____

_____

_____

_____

People to keep in my prayers today.

KEEP communicating with God today

A kind deed done today.	Blessings I received today
_____	_____
_____	_____
_____	_____
_____	_____
_____	_____

The Word became flesh and made his dwelling among us. We have seen his glory, the glory of the one and only Son, who came from the Father, full of grace and truth.
John 1:14

My TALK with God today

Day	Date

☐ Morning Prayer	☐ Evening Prayer	Choose one or more

Three Things I am **THANKFUL** for Today:

1.

2.

3.

LET go and let God handle it

ASK

What do I need forgiveness for?

Ask God to help with this challenge today.

I set these intentions for the day:

_____
_____
_____
_____
_____
_____

People to keep in my prayers today.

KEEP communicating with God today

A kind deed done today.	Blessings I received today
_____	_____
_____	_____
_____	_____
_____	_____
_____	_____

Every word of God is flawless; he is a shield to those who take refuge in him.
Proverbs 30:5

My TALK with God today → **Day** **Date**

☐ Morning Prayer	☐ Evening Prayer	Choose one or more	**ASK**

Three Things I am **THANKFUL** for Today:

1.

2.

3.

LET go and let God handle it

I set these intentions for the day:

_____

_____

_____

_____

_____

_____

ASK

What do I need forgiveness for?

Ask God to help with this challenge today.

People to keep in my prayers today.

KEEP communicating with God today

A kind deed done today.

_____

_____

_____

_____

_____

Blessings I received today

_____

_____

_____

_____

The law of the Lord is perfect, refreshing the soul. The statutes of the Lord are trustworthy, making wise the simple. Psalms 19:7

My TALK with God today → **Day**   **Date**

☐	Morning Prayer	☐	Evening Prayer	Choose one or more

ASK

Three Things I am **THANKFUL** for Today:
1.
2.
3.

What do I need forgiveness for?

LET go and let God handle it

Ask God to help with this challenge today.

I set these intentions for the day:

_____

_____

_____

_____

_____

_____

People to keep in my prayers today.

KEEP communicating with God today

A kind deed done today.   **Blessings I received today**

_____   _____

_____   _____

_____   _____

_____   _____

_____   _____

Those who accepted his message were baptized, and about three thousand were added to their number that day.
Acts 2:41

My TALK with God today → **Day**   **Date**

☐ Morning Prayer	☐ Evening Prayer	Choose one or more	**ASK**

Three Things I am **THANKFUL** for Today:

1.

2.

3.

What do I need forgiveness for?

LET go and let God handle it

Ask God to help with this challenge today.

I set these intentions for the day:
_____
_____
_____
_____
_____
_____

People to keep in my prayers today.

KEEP communicating with God today

A kind deed done today.
_____
_____
_____
_____
_____

Blessings I received today
_____
_____
_____
_____
_____

Teach us to number our days, that we may gain a heart of wisdom.
Psalms 90:12

My TALK with God today

Day

Date

☐ Morning Prayer	☐ Evening Prayer	Choose one or more

Three Things I am **THANKFUL** for Today:

1.

2.

3.

What do I need forgiveness for?

LET go and let God handle it

Ask God to help with this challenge today.

I set these intentions for the day:

_____

_____

_____

_____

_____

_____

People to keep in my prayers today.

KEEP communicating with God today

A kind deed done today.

_____

_____

_____

_____

_____

Blessings I received today

_____

_____

_____

_____

_____

Therefore, if anyone is in Christ, the new creation has come: The old has gone, the new is here!
2 Corinthians 5:17

My TALK with God today

Day _____ **Date** _____

☐ Morning Prayer	☐ Evening Prayer	Choose one or more

ASK

Three Things I am THANKFUL for Today:

1.

2.

3.

What do I need forgiveness for?

LET go and let God handle it

Ask God to help with this challenge today.

I set these intentions for the day:

_____

_____

_____

_____

_____

_____

People to keep in my prayers today.

KEEP communicating with God today

A kind deed done today.

_____

_____

_____

_____

_____

Blessings I received today

_____

_____

_____

_____

Keep your lives free from the love of money and be content with what you have, because God has said, "Never will I leave you; never will I forsake you."
Hebrews 13:5

My TALK with God today   **Day**   **Date**

☐ Morning Prayer	☐ Evening Prayer	Choose one or more

ASK

Three Things I am THANKFUL for Today:

1.

2.

3.

What do I need forgiveness for?

LET go and let God handle it

Ask God to help with this challenge today.

I set these intentions for the day:

_____

_____

_____

_____

_____

_____

People to keep in my prayers today.

KEEP communicating with God today

A kind deed done today.

_____

_____

_____

_____

_____

Blessings I received today

_____

_____

_____

_____

_____

Great is the Lord and most worthy of praise; his greatness no one can fathom.
Psalms 145:3

My TALK with God today →	**Day**	**Date**

☐ Morning Prayer	☐ Evening Prayer	Choose one or more	**ASK**

Three Things I am **THANKFUL** for Today:

1.

2.

3.

What do I need forgiveness for?

LET go and let God handle it

Ask God to help with this challenge today.

I set these intentions for the day:

_____

_____

_____

_____

_____

_____

People to keep in my prayers today.

KEEP communicating with God today

A kind deed done today.

_____   _____

_____   _____

_____   _____

_____   _____

_____   _____

Blessings I received today

The wise in heart accept commands, but a chattering fool comes to ruin.
Proverbs 10:8

My TALK with God today | **Day** | **Date**

☐ Morning Prayer | ☐ Evening Prayer | Choose one or more

What do I need forgiveness for?

Three Things I am **THANKFUL** for Today:

1.

2.

3.

LET go and let God handle it

Ask God to help with this challenge today.

I set these intentions for the day:

_____

_____

_____

_____

_____

_____

People to keep in my prayers today.

KEEP communicating with God today

A kind deed done today. | **Blessings I received today**

_____ | _____

_____ | _____

_____ | _____

_____ | _____

All this also comes from the Lord Almighty, whose plan is wonderful, whose wisdom is magnificent.
Isaiah 28:29

My TALK with God today | **Day** | **Date**

☐ Morning Prayer	☐ Evening Prayer	Choose one or more

Three Things I am **THANKFUL** for Today:

1.

2.

3.

What do I need forgiveness for?

LET go and let God handle it

Ask God to help with this challenge today.

I set these intentions for the day:

_____

_____

_____

_____

_____

_____

People to keep in my prayers today.

KEEP communicating with God today

A kind deed done today.

_____

_____

_____

_____

_____

Blessings I received today

_____

_____

_____

_____

_____

Many are the plans in a person's heart, but it is the Lord's purpose that prevails.
Proverbs 19:21

My TALK with God today → **Day** **Date**

☐ Morning Prayer	☐ Evening Prayer	Choose one or more

ASK

Three Things I am **THANKFUL** for Today:

1.

2.

3.

What do I need forgiveness for?

LET go and let God handle it

Ask God to help with this challenge today.

I set these intentions for the day:

_____

_____

_____

_____

_____

_____

People to keep in my prayers today.

KEEP communicating with God today

A kind deed done today.

_____

_____

_____

_____

_____

Blessings I received today

_____

_____

_____

_____

_____

Our God is in heaven;
he does whatever
pleases him.
Psalms 115:3

My TALK with God today → **Day**   **Date**

☐ Morning Prayer	☐ Evening Prayer	Choose one or more

ASK

Three Things I am **THANKFUL** for Today:
1.
2.
3.

What do I need forgiveness for?

LET go and let God handle it

Ask God to help with this challenge today.

I set these intentions for the day:

_____

_____

_____

_____

_____

_____

People to keep in my prayers today.

KEEP communicating with God today

A kind deed done today.

_____

_____

_____

_____

_____

Blessings I received today

_____

_____

_____

_____

_____

Therefore go and make disciples of all nations, baptizing them in the name of the Father and of the Son and of the Holy Spirit, and teaching them to obey everything I have commanded you. And surely I am with you always, to the very end of the age.
Matthew 28:19-20

My TALK with God today → **Day**   **Date**

☐ Morning Prayer	☐ Evening Prayer	Choose one or more

ASK

Three Things I am **THANKFUL** for Today:

1.

2.

3.

What do I need forgiveness for?

LET go and let God handle it

Ask God to help with this challenge today.

I set these intentions for the day:

_____

_____

_____

_____

_____

_____

People to keep in my prayers today.

KEEP communicating with God today

A kind deed done today.

_____

_____

_____

_____

Blessings I received today

_____

_____

_____

_____

God will repay each person according to what they have done. Romans 2:6

My TALK with God today	Day	Date

☐ Morning Prayer	☐ Evening Prayer	Choose one or more	ASK

Three Things I am **THANKFUL** for Today:

1.

2.

3.

LET go and let God handle it

ASK

What do I need forgiveness for?

Ask God to help with this challenge today.

I set these intentions for the day:

_____

_____

_____

_____

_____

_____

People to keep in my prayers today.

KEEP communicating with God today

A kind deed done today.

_____

_____

_____

_____

_____

Blessings I received today

_____

_____

_____

_____

_____

You must teach what is appropriate to sound doctrine.
Titus 2:1

My TALK with God today **Day** | **Date**

☐	Morning Prayer	☐	Evening Prayer	Choose one or more

ASK

Three Things I am **THANKFUL** for Today:

1.

2.

3.

What do I need forgiveness for?

LET go and let God handle it

Ask God to help with this challenge today.

I set these intentions for the day:

_____

_____

_____

_____

_____

_____

People to keep in my prayers today.

KEEP communicating with God today

A kind deed done today. | **Blessings I received today**

_____ | _____

_____ | _____

_____ | _____

_____ | _____

_____ | _____

I have not hesitated to preach anything that would be helpful to you but have taught you publicly and from house to house.
Acts 20:20

My TALK with God today

Day

Date

☐	Morning Prayer	☐	Evening Prayer	Choose one or more

ASK

Three Things I am **THANKFUL** for Today:

1.

2.

3.

What do I need forgiveness for?

LET go and let God handle it

Ask God to help with this challenge today.

I set these intentions for the day:

_____

_____

_____

_____

_____

_____

People to keep in my prayers today.

KEEP communicating with God today

A kind deed done today.

Blessings I received today

_____   _____

_____   _____

_____   _____

_____   _____

_____   _____

Good and upright is the Lord; therefore he instructs sinners in his ways. He guides the humble in what is right and teaches them his way.
Psalms 25:8-9

My TALK with God today	**Day**	**Date**

☐ Morning Prayer	☐ Evening Prayer	Choose one or more	**ASK**

Three Things I am **THANKFUL** for Today:

1.

2.

3.

LET go and let God handle it

What do I need forgiveness for?

Ask God to help with this challenge today.

I set these intentions for the day:

_____

_____

_____

_____

_____

People to keep in my prayers today.

KEEP communicating with God today

A kind deed done today.

_____

_____

_____

_____

_____

Blessings I received today

_____

_____

_____

_____

_____

The light shines in the darkness, and the darkness has not overcome it.
John 1:5

My TALK with God today

Day

Date

☐ Morning Prayer	☐ Evening Prayer	Choose one or more

ASK

Three Things I am **THANKFUL** for Today:

1.

2.

3.

What do I need forgiveness for?

LET go and let God handle it

Ask God to help with this challenge today.

I set these intentions for the day:

_____

_____

_____

_____

_____

_____

People to keep in my prayers today.

KEEP communicating with God today

A kind deed done today.

_____

_____

_____

_____

_____

Blessings I received today

_____

_____

_____

_____

_____

The name of the righteous is used in blessings, but the name of the wicked will rot.
Proverbs 10:7

My TALK with God today | **Day** | **Date**

☐ Morning Prayer	☐ Evening Prayer	Choose one or more

ASK

Three Things I am **THANKFUL** for Today:

1.

2.

3.

What do I need forgiveness for?

LET go and let God handle it

Ask God to help with this challenge today.

I set these intentions for the day:

_____

_____

_____

_____

_____

_____

People to keep in my prayers today.

KEEP communicating with God today

A kind deed done today.

Blessings I received today

_____ _____

_____ _____

_____ _____

_____ _____

_____ _____

He reveals deep and hidden things; he knows what lies in darkness, and light dwells with him. Daniel 2:22

My TALK with God today   Day

Date

☐ Morning Prayer	☐ Evening Prayer	Choose one or more

ASK

Three Things I am **THANKFUL** for Today:

1.

2.

3.

What do I need forgiveness for?

LET go and let God handle it

Ask God to help with this challenge today.

I set these intentions for the day:

_____

_____

_____

_____

_____

_____

People to keep in my prayers today.

KEEP communicating with God today

A kind deed done today.

Blessings I received today

_____ _____

_____ _____

_____ _____

_____ _____

_____ _____

Pray that the eyes of your heart may be enlightened in order that you may know the hope to which he has called you, the riches of his glorious inheritance in his holy people.
Ephesians 1:18

My TALK with God today → **Day**   **Date**

☐ Morning Prayer	☐ Evening Prayer	Choose one or more

ASK

Three Things I am **THANKFUL** for Today:

1.

2.

3.

What do I need forgiveness for?

LET go and let God handle it

Ask God to help with this challenge today.

I set these intentions for the day:

_____

_____

_____

_____

_____

_____

People to keep in my prayers today.

KEEP communicating with God today

A kind deed done today.   **Blessings I received today**

_____   _____

_____   _____

_____   _____

_____   _____

_____   _____

No one lights a lamp and hides it in a clay jar or puts it under a bed. Instead, they put it on a stand, so that those who come in can see the light.
Luke 8:16

My TALK with God today   **Day**   **Date**

☐ Morning Prayer	☐ Evening Prayer	Choose one or more

ASK

Three Things I am **THANKFUL** for Today:
1.
2.
3.

What do I need forgiveness for?

LET go and let God handle it

Ask God to help with this challenge today.

I set these intentions for the day:

_____

_____

_____

_____

_____

_____

People to keep in my prayers today.

KEEP communicating with God today

A kind deed done today.   Blessings I received today
_____   _____
_____   _____
_____   _____
_____   _____
_____   _____

Every good and perfect gift is from above, coming down from the Father of the heavenly lights, who does not change like shifting shadows.
James 1:17

My TALK with God today ➤ **Day** _____ **Date** _____

☐ Morning Prayer	☐ Evening Prayer	Choose one or more

ASK

Three Things I am **THANKFUL** for Today:

1.

2.

3.

What do I need forgiveness for?

LET go and let God handle it

Ask God to help with this challenge today.

I set these intentions for the day:

_____

_____

_____

_____

_____

_____

People to keep in my prayers today.

KEEP communicating with God today

A kind deed done today.

_____

_____

_____

_____

_____

Blessings I received today

_____

_____

_____

_____

_____

It was not by their sword that they won the land, nor did their arm bring them victory; it was your right hand, your arm, and the light of your face, for you loved them.
Psalms 44:3

My TALK with God today → **Day**   **Date**

☐ Morning Prayer	☐ Evening Prayer	Choose one or more

ASK

Three Things I am **THANKFUL** for Today:

1.

2.

3.

What do I need forgiveness for?

LET go and let God handle it

Ask God to help with this challenge today.

I set these intentions for the day:

_____

_____

_____

_____

_____

_____

People to keep in my prayers today.

KEEP communicating with God today

A kind deed done today.

_____

_____

_____

_____

_____

Blessings I received today

_____

_____

_____

_____

_____

The grace of the Lord Jesus be with God's people.
Revelation 22:21

My TALK with God today | **Day** | **Date**

☐ Morning Prayer	☐ Evening Prayer	Choose one or more

ASK

Three Things I am **THANKFUL** for Today:

1.

2.

3.

What do I need forgiveness for?

LET go and let God handle it

Ask God to help with this challenge today.

I set these intentions for the day:

_____

_____

_____

_____

_____

_____

People to keep in my prayers today.

KEEP communicating with God today

A kind deed done today.

_____

_____

_____

_____

_____

Blessings I received today

_____

_____

_____

_____

He holds success in store for the upright, he is a shield to those whose walk is blameless.
Proverbs 2:7

My TALK with God today | **Day** | **Date**

☐ Morning Prayer	☐ Evening Prayer	Choose one or more	**ASK**

Three Things I am **THANKFUL** for Today:

1.

2.

3.

LET go and let God handle it

What do I need forgiveness for?

Ask God to help with this challenge today.

I set these intentions for the day:
_____
_____
_____
_____
_____
_____

People to keep in my prayers today.

KEEP communicating with God today

A kind deed done today.
_____
_____
_____
_____
_____

Blessings I received today
_____
_____
_____
_____
_____

Shine, for your light has come, and the glory of the Lord rises upon you.
Isaiah 60:1

My TALK with God today | **Day** | **Date**

| ☐ Morning Prayer | ☐ Evening Prayer | Choose one or more |

ASK

Three Things I am THANKFUL for Today:

1.

2.

3.

What do I need forgiveness for?

LET go and let God handle it

Ask God to help with this challenge today.

I set these intentions for the day:

_____

_____

_____

_____

_____

_____

People to keep in my prayers today.

KEEP communicating with God today

A kind deed done today. | **Blessings I received today**

_____ | _____

_____ | _____

_____ | _____

_____ | _____

Blessed is the man who perseveres under trial, because when he has stood the test, he will receive the crown of life that God has promised to those who love him.
James 1:12

My TALK with God today	Day		Date

☐ Morning Prayer	☐ Evening Prayer	Choose one or more	ASK

Three Things I am THANKFUL for Today:

1.

2.

3.

What do I need forgiveness for?

LET go and let God handle it

Ask God to help with this challenge today.

I set these intentions for the day:

_____

_____

_____

_____

_____

People to keep in my prayers today.

KEEP communicating with God today

A kind deed done today.

_____

_____

_____

_____

_____

Blessings I received today

_____

_____

_____

_____

_____

Gentleness and self-control. Against such things there is no law.
Galatians 5:23

My TALK with God today → **Day** **Date**

☐ Morning Prayer	☐ Evening Prayer	Choose one or more

ASK

Three Things I am **THANKFUL** for Today:
1.
2.
3.

What do I need forgiveness for?

LET go and let God handle it

Ask God to help with this challenge today.

I set these intentions for the day:

_____

_____

_____

_____

_____

_____

People to keep in my prayers today.

KEEP communicating with God today

A kind deed done today.	Blessings I received today
_____	_____
_____	_____
_____	_____
_____	_____
_____	_____

Surely your goodness and love will follow me all the days of my life, and I will dwell in the house of the Lord forever.
Psalms 23:6

My TALK with God today   **Day**   **Date**

☐ Morning Prayer	☐ Evening Prayer	Choose one or more

ASK

Three Things I am **THANKFUL** for Today:
1.
2.
3.

What do I need
forgiveness for?

LET go and let God handle it

Ask God to help with this
challenge today.

I set these intentions for the day:

_____

_____

_____

_____

_____

_____

People to keep in my
prayers today.

KEEP communicating with God today

A kind deed done today.   **Blessings I received today**

_____   _____

_____   _____

_____   _____

_____   _____

_____   _____

Rend your heart and not
your garments. Return to
the Lord your God, for he
is gracious and
compassionate, slow to
anger and abounding in
love, and he relents from
sending calamity.
Joel 2:13

My TALK with God today → **Day**   **Date**

☐ Morning Prayer	☐ Evening Prayer	Choose one or more

What do I need forgiveness for?

Three Things I am **THANKFUL** for Today:

1.

2.

3.

LET go and let God handle it

Ask God to help with this challenge today.

I set these intentions for the day:

_____

_____

_____

_____

_____

_____

People to keep in my prayers today.

KEEP communicating with God today

A kind deed done today.   Blessings I received today

_____   _____

_____   _____

_____   _____

_____   _____

Grace and peace to you from God our Father and from the Lord Jesus Christ. Romans 1:7

My TALK with God today → **Day**   **Date**

☐ Morning Prayer	☐ Evening Prayer	Choose one or more

ASK

Three Things I am **THANKFUL** for Today:

1.

2.

3.

What do I need forgiveness for?

LET go and let God handle it

Ask God to help with this challenge today.

I set these intentions for the day:

_____
_____
_____
_____
_____
_____

People to keep in my prayers today.

KEEP communicating with God today

A kind deed done today.   Blessings I received today

_____   _____
_____   _____
_____   _____
_____   _____
_____   _____

The Lord bless you and keep you; the Lord make his face shine on you and be gracious to you; the Lord turn his face toward you and give you peace.
Numbers 6:24-26

My TALK with God today | Day | Date

☐ Morning Prayer | ☐ Evening Prayer | Choose one or more

ASK

Three Things I am **THANKFUL** for Today:

1.

2.

3.

What do I need forgiveness for?

LET go and let God handle it

Ask God to help with this challenge today.

I set these intentions for the day:

_____

_____

_____

_____

_____

_____

People to keep in my prayers today.

KEEP communicating with God today

A kind deed done today.

_____

_____

_____

_____

_____

Blessings I received today

_____

_____

_____

_____

_____

Blessed is the one who does not walk in step with the wicked or stand in the way that sinners take or sit in the company of mockers.
Psalms 1:1

My TALK with God today → **Day**   **Date**

☐ Morning Prayer	☐ Evening Prayer	Choose one or more

ASK

Three Things I am **THANKFUL** for Today:

1.

2.

3.

What do I need forgiveness for?

LET go and let God handle it

Ask God to help with this challenge today.

I set these intentions for the day:

_____

_____

_____

_____

_____

_____

People to keep in my prayers today.

KEEP communicating with God today

A kind deed done today.   **Blessings I received today**

_____   _____

_____   _____

_____   _____

_____   _____

_____   _____

Blessed are
the pure in heart,
for they will
see God.
Matthew 5:8

My TALK with God today → **Day** | **Date**

☐ Morning Prayer	☐ Evening Prayer	Choose one or more

ASK

Three Things I am **THANKFUL** for Today:
1.
2.
3.

What do I need forgiveness for?

LET go and let God handle it

Ask God to help with this challenge today.

I set these intentions for the day:

_____

_____

_____

_____

_____

People to keep in my prayers today.

KEEP communicating with God today

A kind deed done today.

_____

_____

_____

_____

_____

Blessings I received today

_____

_____

_____

_____

_____

Observe what the Lord your God requires: Walk in obedience to him, and keep his decrees and commands, his laws and regulations, as written in the Law of Moses. Do this so that you may prosper in all you do and wherever you go.
1 Kings 2:3

My TALK with God today

Day

Date

☐ **Morning Prayer** | ☐ **Evening Prayer** | Choose one or more | **ASK**

Three Things I am **THANKFUL** for Today:
1.
2.
3.

What do I need forgiveness for?

LET go and let God handle it

Ask God to help with this challenge today.

I set these intentions for the day:

_____

_____

_____

_____

_____

_____

People to keep in my prayers today.

KEEP communicating with God today

A kind deed done today.

_____

_____

_____

_____

Blessings I received today

_____

_____

_____

_____

The tongue has the power of life and death, and those who love it will eat its fruit. Proverbs 18:21

My TALK with God today

Day

Date

☐ Morning Prayer	☐ Evening Prayer	Choose one or more

ASK

Three Things I am **THANKFUL** for Today:

1.

2.

3.

What do I need forgiveness for?

LET go and let God handle it

Ask God to help with this challenge today.

I set these intentions for the day:

_____

_____

_____

_____

_____

_____

People to keep in my prayers today.

KEEP communicating with God today

A kind deed done today.

_____

_____

_____

_____

_____

Blessings I received today

_____

_____

_____

_____

_____

Cast all your anxiety on him because he cares for you.
1 Peter 5:7

My TALK with God today ➤ Day   Date

☐ Morning Prayer	☐ Evening Prayer	Choose one or more

Three Things I am **THANKFUL** for Today:

1.

2.

3.

LET go and let God handle it

I set these intentions for the day:

_____

_____

_____

_____

_____

KEEP communicating with God today

A kind deed done today.

_____

_____

_____

_____

_____

Blessings I received today

_____

_____

_____

_____

_____

ASK

What do I need forgiveness for?

Ask God to help with this challenge today.

People to keep in my prayers today.

God made him who had no sin to be sin for us, so that in him we might become the righteousness of God. 2 Corinthians 5:21

My TALK with God today

Day

Date

☐ Morning Prayer	☐ Evening Prayer	Choose one or more

ASK

Three Things I am **THANKFUL** for Today:

1.

2.

3.

LET go and let God handle it

What do I need forgiveness for?

Ask God to help with this challenge today.

I set these intentions for the day:

_____

_____

_____

_____

_____

_____

People to keep in my prayers today.

KEEP communicating with God today

A kind deed done today.

Blessings I received today

_____ _____

_____ _____

_____ _____

_____ _____

_____ _____

Blessed is the nation whose God is the Lord, the people he chose for his inheritance.
Psalms 33:12

My TALK with God today → **Day** **Date**

☐ Morning Prayer	☐ Evening Prayer	Choose one or more

ASK

Three Things I am **THANKFUL** for Today:

1.

2.

3.

What do I need forgiveness for?

LET go and let God handle it

Ask God to help with this challenge today.

I set these intentions for the day:

_____

_____

_____

_____

_____

_____

People to keep in my prayers today.

KEEP communicating with God today

A kind deed done today.

_____

_____

_____

_____

_____

Blessings I received today

_____

_____

_____

_____

_____

After they had fasted and prayed, they placed their hands on them and sent.
Acts 13:3

My TALK with God today

Day _____ **Date** _____

☐ Morning Prayer	☐ Evening Prayer	Choose one or more

ASK

Three Things I am **THANKFUL** for Today:
1.
2.
3.

What do I need forgiveness for?

LET go and let God handle it

Ask God to help with this challenge today.

I set these intentions for the day:

_____

_____

_____

_____

_____

_____

People to keep in my prayers today.

KEEP communicating with God today

A kind deed done today.

_____

_____

_____

_____

_____

Blessings I received today

_____

_____

_____

_____

Blessed are you when people hate you, when they exclude you and insult you and reject your name as evil, because of the Son of Man.
Luke 6:22

My TALK with God today

Day

Date

☐ Morning Prayer

☐ Evening Prayer

Choose one or more

ASK

Three Things I am **THANKFUL** for Today:

1.

2.

3.

What do I need forgiveness for?

LET go and let God handle it

Ask God to help with this challenge today.

I set these intentions for the day:

People to keep in my prayers today.

KEEP communicating with God today

A kind deed done today.

Blessings I received today

What is mankind that you are mindful of them, human beings that you care for them?
Psalms 8:4

My TALK with God today   **Day**   **Date**

☐ Morning Prayer	☐ Evening Prayer	Choose one or more

ASK

Three Things I am **THANKFUL** for Today:

1.

2.

3.

What do I need forgiveness for?

LET go and let God handle it

Ask God to help with this challenge today.

I set these intentions for the day:

_____

_____

_____

_____

_____

_____

People to keep in my prayers today.

KEEP communicating with God today

A kind deed done today.   Blessings I received today

_____   _____

_____   _____

_____   _____

_____   _____

_____   _____

Blessed is the one whom God corrects; so do not despise the discipline of the Almighty. Job 5:17

My TALK with God today → **Day** **Date**

☐ Morning Prayer	☐ Evening Prayer	Choose one or more

ASK

Three Things I am **THANKFUL** for Today:

1.

2.

3.

What do I need forgiveness for?

LET go and let God handle it

Ask God to help with this challenge today.

I set these intentions for the day:

_____

_____

_____

_____

_____

_____

People to keep in my prayers today.

KEEP communicating with God today

A kind deed done today.   Blessings I received today

_____   _____

_____   _____

_____   _____

_____   _____

_____   _____

Blessed are you when people insult you, persecute you and falsely say all kinds of evil against you because of me.
Matthew 5:11

My TALK with God today → **Day** **Date**

☐ Morning Prayer	☐ Evening Prayer	Choose one or more

ASK

Three Things I am **THANKFUL** for Today:
1.
2.
3.

What do I need forgiveness for?

LET go and let God handle it

Ask God to help with this challenge today.

I set these intentions for the day:

_____

_____

_____

_____

_____

_____

People to keep in my prayers today.

KEEP communicating with God today

A kind deed done today.

_____

_____

_____

_____

Blessings I received today

_____

_____

_____

_____

When God raised up his servant, he sent him first to you to bless you by turning each of you from your wicked ways.
Acts 3:26

My TALK with God today	Day		Date

☐ Morning Prayer	☐ Evening Prayer	Choose one or more	**ASK**

Three Things I am **THANKFUL** for Today:

1.

2.

3.

What do I need forgiveness for?

LET go and let God handle it

Ask God to help with this challenge today.

I set these intentions for the day:
_____
_____
_____
_____
_____
_____

People to keep in my prayers today.

KEEP communicating with God today

A kind deed done today.

_____
_____
_____
_____
_____

Blessings I received today

_____
_____
_____
_____
_____

The heavens declare the glory of God; the skies proclaim the work of his hands. Day after day they pour forth speech; night after night they reveal knowledge.
Psalms 19:1-2

My TALK with God today → **Day**   **Date**

☐ Morning Prayer	☐ Evening Prayer	Choose one or more

ASK

Three Things I am **THANKFUL** for Today:

1.

2.

3.

What do I need forgiveness for?

LET go and let God handle it

Ask God to help with this challenge today.

I set these intentions for the day:

_____

_____

_____

_____

_____

_____

People to keep in my prayers today.

KEEP communicating with God today

A kind deed done today.   Blessings I received today

_____   _____

_____   _____

_____   _____

_____   _____

_____   _____

Truly I tell you, if you have faith as small as a mustard seed, you can say to this mountain, 'Move from here to there,' and it will move. Nothing will be impossible for you.
Matthew 17:20

My TALK with God today → **Day** **Date**

☐ Morning Prayer	☐ Evening Prayer	Choose one or more

ASK

Three Things I am **THANKFUL** for Today:

1.

2.

3.

LET go and let God handle it

What do I need forgiveness for?

Ask God to help with this challenge today.

I set these intentions for the day:

_____

_____

_____

_____

_____

_____

People to keep in my prayers today.

KEEP communicating with God today

A kind deed done today.

_____

_____

_____

_____

_____

Blessings I received today

_____

_____

_____

_____

_____

There is one body and one Spirit, just as you were called to one hope when you were called.
Ephesians 4:4

My TALK with God today | **Day** | **Date**

☐ Morning Prayer	☐ Evening Prayer	Choose one or more

ASK

Three Things I am **THANKFUL** for Today:

1.

2.

3.

What do I need forgiveness for?

LET go and let God handle it

Ask God to help with this challenge today.

I set these intentions for the day:

_____

_____

_____

_____

_____

_____

People to keep in my prayers today.

KEEP communicating with God today

A kind deed done today.

_____

_____

_____

_____

_____

Blessings I received today

_____

_____

_____

_____

_____

Love does not delight in evil but rejoices with the truth. It always protects, always trusts, always hopes, always perseveres.
1 Corinthians 13:6-7

My TALK with God today → Day _____ Date _____

☐ Morning Prayer	☐ Evening Prayer	Choose one or more

ASK

What do I need forgiveness for?

Three Things I am **THANKFUL** for Today:
1.
2.
3.

LET go and let God handle it

Ask God to help with this challenge today.

I set these intentions for the day:

_____

_____

_____

_____

_____

_____

People to keep in my prayers today.

KEEP communicating with God today

A kind deed done today.

_____

_____

_____

_____

_____

Blessings I received today

_____

_____

_____

_____

_____

Peace I leave with you; my peace I give you. I do not give to you as the world gives. Do not let your hearts be troubled and do not be afraid. John 14:27

My TALK with God today

Day

Date

☐ Morning Prayer	☐ Evening Prayer	Choose one or more

ASK

What do I need forgiveness for?

Three Things I am **THANKFUL** for Today:

1.

2.

3.

LET go and let God handle it

Ask God to help with this challenge today.

I set these intentions for the day:

_____

_____

_____

_____

_____

People to keep in my prayers today.

KEEP communicating with God today

A kind deed done today.

_____

_____

_____

_____

_____

Blessings I received today

_____

_____

_____

_____

_____

Do not wear yourself out to get rich; do not trust your own cleverness.
Proverbs 23:4

My TALK with God today ➤ **Day** **Date**

☐ Morning Prayer	☐ Evening Prayer	Choose one or more

ASK

Three Things I am **THANKFUL** for Today:

1.

2.

3.

What do I need forgiveness for?

LET go and let God handle it

Ask God to help with this challenge today.

I set these intentions for the day:

_____

_____

_____

People to keep in my prayers today.

_____

_____

_____

KEEP communicating with God today

A kind deed done today.

_____

_____

_____

_____

_____

Blessings I received today

_____

_____

_____

_____

_____

Watch and pray so that you will not fall into temptation. The spirit is willing, but the flesh is weak. Matthew 26:41

My TALK with God today	Day		Date

☐ Morning Prayer	☐ Evening Prayer	Choose one or more

ASK

Three Things I am **THANKFUL** for Today:

1.

2.

3.

What do I need forgiveness for?

LET go and let God handle it

Ask God to help with this challenge today.

I set these intentions for the day:

_____

_____

_____

_____

_____

People to keep in my prayers today.

KEEP communicating with God today

A kind deed done today.

_____

_____

_____

_____

_____

Blessings I received today

_____

_____

_____

_____

_____

When I am afraid, I put my trust in you.
Psalms 56:3

My TALK with God today	**Day**	**Date**

☐ **Morning Prayer**	☐ **Evening Prayer**	Choose one or more	**ASK**

Three Things I am **THANKFUL** for Today:

1.

2.

3.

LET go and let God handle it

What do I need forgiveness for?

Ask God to help with this challenge today.

I set these intentions for the day:

_____

_____

_____

_____

_____

_____

People to keep in my prayers today.

KEEP communicating with God today

A kind deed done today.

_____

_____

_____

_____

Blessings I received today

_____

_____

_____

_____

Therefore we do not lose heart. Though outwardly we are wasting away, yet inwardly we are being renewed day by day.
2 Corinthians 4:16

My TALK with God today **Day** **Date**

☐	Morning Prayer	☐	Evening Prayer	Choose one or more

ASK

Three Things I am **THANKFUL** for Today:

1.

2.

3.

What do I need forgiveness for?

LET go and let God handle it

Ask God to help with this challenge today.

I set these intentions for the day:

_____

_____

_____

_____

_____

_____

People to keep in my prayers today.

KEEP communicating with God today

A kind deed done today.

_____

_____

_____

_____

_____

Blessings I received today

_____

_____

_____

_____

_____

For it has been granted to you on behalf of Christ not only to believe in him, but also to suffer for him. Philippians 1:29

My TALK with God today　　　**Day**　　　　　　　　**Date**

☐	Morning Prayer	☐	Evening Prayer	Choose one or more	**ASK**

Three Things I am **THANKFUL** for Today:

1.

2.

3.

LET go and let God handle it

What do I need forgiveness for?

Ask God to help with this challenge today.

I set these intentions for the day:

_____

_____

_____

_____

_____

_____

People to keep in my prayers today.

KEEP communicating with God today

A kind deed done today.　　　Blessings I received today

_____　　_____

_____　　_____

_____　　_____

_____　　_____

_____　　_____

When hard pressed, I cried to the Lord; he brought me into a spacious place.
Psalms 118:5

My TALK with God today → **Day**

Date

☐ Morning Prayer	☐ Evening Prayer	Choose one or more

ASK

Three Things I am **THANKFUL** for Today:

1.

2.

3.

What do I need forgiveness for?

LET go and let God handle it

Ask God to help with this challenge today.

I set these intentions for the day:

_____

_____

_____

_____

_____

_____

People to keep in my prayers today.

KEEP communicating with God today

A kind deed done today.

_____

_____

_____

_____

_____

Blessings I received today

_____

_____

_____

_____

_____

Whoever heeds discipline shows the way to life, but whoever ignores correction leads others astray.
Proverbs 10:17